1998 Beanie Collector's Handbook

The Premier Source for Up-to-Date Pricing and Information

Published by

Trend Masters Publication • Grand Rapids, Michigan

Publisher: Jeffrey R. Beckett

Editor: Jay Johnson

Art Director: Lisa O'Neill

Assistant Editor: Sharon E. Johnson

Contributing Editors: Jeff Czerniakowski, Kim Goddard, Vicky Krupka

Photography: Rebecca Reed, Daniel Harris, Jeff Sciortino

Cover photo by Jeff Sciortino

Back Cover photo by Rebecca Reed

Published by
Trend Masters Publication
2432 Oakwood Drive SE
Grand Rapids, MI 49506

Manufactured in the United States of America

ISBN: 0-9662573-0-8

First Edition: February 1998

10 9 8 7 6 5 4 3 2 1

This book is an independent work, and is not authorized, endorsed or sponsored by TY Inc.

Table of Contents

History of Beanie Babies

by Vicky Krupka

When does a regional trend become a national obsession? When does a hobby become a 24-hour-a-day addiction?

Is it when a simple stuffed animal inspires a frenzy? Is it when mothers set up stakeouts for UPS delivery trucks? Is it when the creator is forced into virtual seclusion? Is it when the manufacturer delists its phone number to free up its switchboard from thousands of phone calls? Is it when a fast food chain includes a toy with its kids' meals, and enough food to feed the starving masses of India is discarded untouched to obtain the precious fabric fish?

When it comes to Beanie Babies, the answer is: all of the above.

These "must have" toys appeal as much to adults as they do kids. Many families have two collections — one for the adults to display, and one for children to play with. Gender and age-neutral, Beanie Babies cross all boundaries; their appeal is broadly based — loved by children, college students, parents, and grandparents alike. Boys are almost as obsessed with the animals as girls, although they tend to prefer more male-oriented models such as Crunch, Tank and Spike. Parents especially like them for children because they are simple — no computer chips or batteries — and they provide hours of imaginative fun.

Beanie Babies are the creation of Ty Warner, founder and sole owner of the privately held Ty Inc. of Oak Brook, Ill. The 50ish Warner, a 30-year toy industry veteran, has run his own stuffed animal company since 1985. A native of Illinois and 1962 graduate of Kalamazoo College, Warner once worked for Dakin Inc., where he sold stuffed animals to specialty gift shops.

"That taught me that it's better selling 40,000 accounts that it is five accounts," he told *Forbes* magazine in 1996, shortly before he stopped talking to the press. "It's more difficult to do, but for the longevity of the company and the profit margins, it's the better of the two."

Warner quit Dakin in 1980 and spent a few years in Italy before designing a line of inexpensive, understuffed, floppy Himalayan cats. He launched the line primarily by selling to his former Dakin customers. His new venture, dubbed Ty Inc., manufactured an entire line of plush and stuffed collectibles. But realizing there was also a market for low-cost, pocket-sized toys that kids could buy with their own allowance money, he created the Beanie Babies Collection in 1993.

Manufactured by independent factories in China and Korea, Beanie Babies are plush-covered bean bag animals, stuffed with fiberfill and small PVC pellets (polyvinyl chloride pellets, the modern equivalent of beans). Each Beanie is uniquely poseable, purposely understuffed, and comes with a

Ty Warner, founder and owner of Ty Inc., and the creative genius behind the Beanie Babies.

distinctive red heart swing tag that lists the animal's name, birthday and a cute personalized poem. The appeal is simple: not only can they fit into a pocket, but at a retail price of about $5 each, they are a consumer's dream — the perfect combination of personality and price.

The Original Nine

The first nine Beanie Babies were introduced in January 1994. They were Legs the Frog, Squealer the Pig, Cubbie the Bear, Flash the Dolphin, Splash the Whale, Patti the Platypus, Chocolate the Moose, Spot the Dog and Pinchers the Lobster. Because of the overwhelming response to these nine Beanies, several new designs were created and introduced the following June.

Of the original nine Beanies, the only ones not currently in production are Flash and Splash, who were retired May 1997. Since the introduction of the product line, new Beanies have been introduced twice a year. Typically, this happens in January and again in mid-year, usually around June 1st. The periodic introduction of new styles not only attracts new customers, it allows old customers to continue adding to their ever-growing collections.

A unique feature of this line of stuffed animals is that, starting January 1995, Beanies have been officially retired on a regular basis. The first to be retired were Chilly, Humphrey, Peking, Slither, Trap, Web, and the colored Teddys — Cranberry, Jade, Magenta, Teal and Violet.

Understandably, all of these Beanies are in high demand by collectors.

Beginning in 1996, Ty initiated the practice of retiring Beanies each time he introduced new ones. This move has caused prices on the secondary market to soar for retired, or even rumored "soon-to-be" retired Beanies. On Jan. 29, 1997, for example, Ty announced the retirement of Radar the Bat and Sparky the Dalmatian, which triggered a buying frenzy for those two animals. The next day Ty recanted and "unretired" the two Beanies, but from that day until the official retirement of Radar and Sparky in May 1997, they became "hard-to-find" Beanies and commanded higher than normal prices on the secondary market.

First introduced in the Chicago area, Beanie Babies became really popular there in the summer of 1995. They didn't develop craze status until the spring and summer of 1996 when, explains company representative Ann Nickels, "they began to take off in the Midwest. This year, in January and February they took off around the rest of the country — the coasts, Texas, Florida. Now we have a distributor for Canada, the UK and Germany."

Explosive Growth

According to Nickels, Ty realized sales increases of 1,000 percent in 1996, and is currently on track to grow another 1,000 percent in 1997. Although Ty Inc. refuses to provide sales figures, *Forbes* in 1996 estimated that

The Original Nine debuted in January 1994 and remained in production until Flash and Splash retired in May.

Ty "seems likely to sell 100 million of the things this year . . . and generate $250 million in (wholesale) sales." *Forbes* touted Ty's invention as "this year's megatoy," and *Playthings magazine (a trade publication* for toy retailers) ranked Beanie Babies as one of the top-10 best selling toys for 1996.

Frank Reysen, editor of *Playthings*, said, "It's a national phenomenon."

To date, there are more than 100 Beanies in the collection, and more than 50 that have been retired. Some of these have undergone style or color changes during their lifetimes, with variations commanding higher prices on the secondary market. For example: Inch the worm with antenna made of felt, not yarn; Derby the horse with a mane of fine yarn versus coarse; and Sly the Fox with a white belly versus brown.

One of the most valued of these variations started out as a factory mistake. In an interview with the *Wheaton* (Ill.) *Press*, Nickels explained the case of Peanut, the Royal Blue elephant that shipped to customers in January 1995.

"A dark blue elephant," Nickels said, "it was actually an error in production and it came in the wrong color. It was supposed to have been in light blue, but it came in dark blue . . . next thing we knew they were worth several thousand dollars."

The toy's popularity is due as much to a few strokes of marketing genius as to its cuddle factor. In what is considered an unorthodox, but brilliant, selling strategy, Beanies are purposely not sold to mass marketers such as WalMart and Toys "R" Us.

The strategy may have cost Ty Inc. orders in the short run, but it created collectibility by allowing the company to keep its supplies in line with demand. Ty also bypassed traditional distributors, relying instead on selling directly to specialty outlets such as card shops, candy stores and novelty shops, as well as hotel, museum and hospital gift shops. Ty's theory is that the harder toys are to obtain, the more people want them. He has yet to be proven wrong.

The peculiar distribution and growth of the Beanie Babies phenomenon highlights another difference between this toy and other megahits of the recent past. Since they are not the brainchild of a toy biz giant such as Hasbro or Mattel, and since they are not the byproduct of some licensing deal with a Disney movie tie-in, Beanie Babies were not launched with a marketing blitz of saturation bombing on Saturday morning television.

Grassroots Growth

Beanie Babies are not advertised in print or on TV, nor do they need to be. Word of mouth is all the advertising Ty needs, and they get plenty of it. Retailers have a hard time even stocking them, often waiting months for an order to be filled, let alone receiving enough Beanies to fill demand. It is not uncommon for a retailer to sell out of a new shipment of thousands of Beanies within days,

even hours, of receipt.

Starting April 1, 1997, Ty made it even harder for retailers to keep large supplies of Beanies on hand by limiting them to a once-a-month order of only 36 of any one kind of Beanie, with no back orders. If a style of Beanie is not in stock at the time an order is filled, that portion of the order is canceled, leaving the retailer to wait until the next month to try again. Despite these limits, orders at Ty are still backed up for weeks and months waiting to clear the mountains of paperwork at headquarters.

Attention Grabbers

While Ty does not advertise its product, that is not to say it hasn't enjoyed media attention. Articles about Beanie Babies constantly appear in newspapers and magazines across the country. Everyone from the Chicago Tribune, The New York Times, The Wall Street Journal, Forbes, People, Newsweek, on down to most local papers have carried an article about the Beanie craze at one time or another. Beanie Babies were even featured on the March 19, 1997, "Today Show" when Karmen Kohlwes, vice president of Ty, gave the country a sneak preview of one of its soon-to-be released new Beanies — Roary the Lion.

Starting in late summer 1996, Ty has provided a page on the Internet (www.ty.com) for Beanie fans to meet and find out more about their favorite toy. The Ty site offers lists of all the Beanie Babies, their birthdays, 101 things to do with Beanies, a monthly profile of a chosen Beanie, as well as a guestbook where fans can post comments or offers to buy and sell Beanies. During the summer of 1996, an Internet search for the phrase "Beanie Babies" pulled up just three "hits." Now, the net has become a major avenue for conveying information about the toys, with literally hundreds of sites to choose from. These sites provide guestbooks, auctions, trading posts, little known Beanie facts, advice, gossip, a wide variety of Beanie accessories, or simply show pictures of proud owners with their collections. Log onto any of these sites day or night, and you're likely to encounter a Beanie soul mate who shares your passion.

It truly is an addiction, but what better way to go?

New In 1998

Britannia
the Bear (European exclusive)
Birthday: Not Available
Value: $50

Bruno
the Terrier
Birthday: Sept. 9, 1997
Value: $6.00

Hissy
the snake
Birthday: April 4, 1997
Value: $6.00

Iggy
the Iguana
Birthday: Aug. 12, 1997
Value: $6.00

Prance
the Cat
Birthday: Nov. 20, 1997
Value: $6.00

Pounce
the Cat
Birthday: Aug. 28,1997
Value: $6.00

Puffer
the Puffin
Birthday: Nov. 3, 1997
Value: $6.00

Rainbow
the Chameleon
Birthday: Oct. 10, 1997
Value: $6.00

Spunky
the Dog
Birthday: Jan. 14, 1997
Value: $6.00

Smoochy
the Frog
Birthday: Oct. 1, 1997
Value: $6.00

Stretch
the Ostrich
Birthday: Sept. 21, 1997
Value: $6.00

Condition Guide

Before you buy or sell, learn to judge a Beanie's condition

the expanding secondary market for Beanie Babies means collectors who aren't armed with a solid understanding of its terms are at a distinct disadvantage.

With Tags. Without Tags. Mint. Slightly Used. You might run into a "bent tag" Patti or a "slightly bent tag" Peanut. Some sellers bill their Beanies as coming from "a smoke-free-environment." Do these conditions affect the quality of the Beanie about to be purchased? Certainly! Here is a quick run-through of how to be a connoisseur of the Beanie Baby secondary market.

Three major factors determine the value of a Beanie Baby: the tags, the condition of the plush, and the condition of the Beanie itself.

The Swing Tag is one of the first determining factors of value. Everyone would like a mint Beanie Baby, but in the secondary market that may not always be possible. Especially with rare Beanie Babies, the chances are good that the swing tag is missing or damaged. This happened quite often before people became aware of the collectibility of Beanies. The animal probably started life as a child's plaything, so the parents naturally cut off the tags.

A current Beanie without its swing tag is worth about half the retail price or less. A recently retired Beanie (especially all 1997 retirees) that runs around the hundred-dollar range in mint condition usually receives a fifty percent markdown without the tag.

The fifty percent rule does not apply with the older retirees. Some purchasers, who may have searched months for a particular Beanie, may not care if there's a swing tag or not. There is a decrease in price, but not so steep. A good example of this is the Spot without the spot. In mint condition, this particular Spot is worth around $1,000. Without the swing tag, Spot without the spot can bring in around $700.

Sometimes the tush tag may be missing as well. In this case, the value is cut drastically (usually by sixty percent and higher), since there is no actual proof that this Beanie is a real Ty Beanie Baby.

If the swing tag is damaged (meaning creased, worn, frayed edges, torn) the markdown depends on the severity. Mildly damage (slightly creased) would cause a drop of $10 to $50, depending on the status or rarity of the Beanie. An obviously damaged tag would decrease the value by as much as a fourth of the mint price. Most of the time, a severely damaged tag (creased or torn) is considered barely a step above a missing tag.

Keep in mind that many parents remove the tag from a Beanie for safe-keeping. The tag may be replaced later to sell the Beanie. It's hard to determine just how much to knock off the value of a Beanie such as this. Technically, it's no longer mint. This is where the condition of the plush should be considered. If the tag looks fine but the plush is worn, the Beanie probably has been retagged, and the price should decrease by about a fourth.

Collectors also may wonder how

by Kim Goddard

to treat a Beanie with a price sticker on the tag. For the most part, this is a little annoyance that must be tolerated and doesn't affect the value, although a sticker in plain view on the front of the tag can depreciate it a little. Attempting to remove the sticker can result in tearing the tag, however, so it's best to leave it alone.

Another factor in determining the value of a Beanie Baby is the quality of its plush. Look for traces of dirt, fibers that aren't shiny (or even a little clumped), and any signs of stitching or repair. If the fibers are clumped and smell like Tide, the Beanie has been washed. In the case of worn plush, the only real guide is your own best judgment. A good starting point, if it is obviously worn, is half the mint value.

One factor often overlooked is a Beanie Baby's environment. Though they don't look like sponges, that is exactly what Beanie Babies are. They absorb smells, smoke and other airborne particles. If the Beanie has an odor or its plush has become discolored, it is no longer mint. The value should be decreased by about a third, for starters.

A Beanie Baby's value is determined by its tags, its plush and its environment. Every situation will be different, and the guidelines for marking down the value may not always hold. Examine the Beanie, make sure that the felt is smooth and feels clean (and not sticky), and smell it for unusual odors. Rub your fingers across the tags to find creases you may not see. Then decide what you feel the Beanie is worth and make an offer.

Beanie Variations

Your favorites may have more than one version

As with any collectible, the oddities and variations in the Beanie Babies product line are the most sought after and coveted of the whole collection.

The reasons that these variations exist are several. First, some Beanies were changed after their introduction to become more functional (i.e. the Quackers with wings stands up much better than the Quackers without wings), because the fabric was no longer available (old Stripes the Tiger), or because they just looked better in a new color (pink Inky is much more attractive than tan Inky). Second, some slipped through production as just plain mistakes (Righty without a flag, Libearty with an upside down flag).

One of the most treasured and unusual variations in my personal collection is Peanut the Elephant in a dark, royal blue fabric. Although this color is shown in small areas on other Beanies, Peanut is the only one in the product line to boast this striking color for his entire body. At first glance, he looks much like a circus elephant. Issued in the fall of 1995 bearing a third generation tag, he was produced in this color for only a couple of months before being replaced by his brother Peanut (bearing

the same style number) in light blue.

Equally hard to find in the market is the original Quackers the Duck #4024, first introduced in summer 1995 without wings. Looking slightly off balance, this cute little duck was first spotted wearing a single heart tag, and he later wore the second generation tag with thin Ty lettering that opens. After only about six months, this Quackers (who had trouble sitting up properly) was replaced by the currently available Quackers with wings.

Spot the Dog (style #4000) is one of the original nine Beanie Babies released in 1993. His first version was unique in that it had *no spot* on his back. The obvious question: "Why is he called Spot?" The obvious answer followed shortly . . . a Spot the Dog proudly displaying a large spot in the middle of his back.

Although most of the Beanies have gone through one revision

by MaryBeth Sobolewski

Learning the difference between an old-face (left) and new-face (right) bear is a must for collectors.

at most, Zip the Black Cat #4004 and Nip the Gold Cat #4003 actually have seen three variations.

Originally introduced in Fall '95 to look like cuddly kittens with full, round faces and bodies, Zip and Nip (referred to as the white-bellied Zip and Nip) had white faces and bellies, solid black or gold paws, pink ears and pink whiskers.

Next in the line up were Zip and Nip with the same product numbers, but much thinner bodies and faces — resembling adult cats more than kittens. Nip now

Many collectors consider the dark blue Peanut their most prized possession.

had an all-gold body, gold face and paws, pink ears and whiskers (commonly referred to as the All-gold Nip). Zip now had an all-black body, black face and paws, pink ears and whiskers (commonly referred to as the All-black Zip). Shortly afterward, the current Zip and Nip were mass produced with solid-color bodies and faces, white ears, white whiskers and white paws.

Inky #4028 is another Beanie Baby that had three variations. First hitting the market in a muted tan color with no mouth and a single first-generation or thin-lettering second generation tag.

Soon enough, tan Inky, bearing the third generation Ty tag, sprouted a mouth! Finally, the Inky we know today was introduced in a bright pink color, which is a favorite of many. One rare variation of the current pink Inky is the octopus with nine instead of eight legs.

Grin and Bear It

Another of my personal favorites is the large collection of Ty Teddy Bears.

The original Teddies hit the market in Spring of 1994 and were a collection of six colored bears sporting faces that look much like the face on the old Disney favorite, Winnie the Pooh. The faces had pointy noses and eyes set close together. Five of the colors were jewel tones: Magenta, Violet, Jade, Cranberry and Teal all had the first and second generation of the Ty hang tag. The last color is the hardest to find in today's market.

Approximately a year later, the New Face bears replaced their earlier friends. These Teddies had faces much like Garcia. The faces were round, the eyes set further apart and each one had a contrasting bow crafted of satin ribbon. Although newer in the product line, these Teddies are actually valued more on the secondary market because of the relatively small quantity of them produced before the colored Teddies were retired together.

Other Beanie Babies underwent drastic changes in color over time. Happy the Hippo (Style #4061) was introduced in 1994 in a medium gray color — functional, yet bland. Some time later he was replaced by the bright lavender Happy the Hippo bearing the same style number.

Digger the Crab (Style #4027) in his original bright orange color is getting very hard to find. Orange Digger's replacement, Red Digger, enjoyed a long run in the stores before he, too, was retired in May 1997.

Lizzy the Lizard (Style #4033) in his original muted tie-dyed fabric is tremendously sought after lately. Although not very attractive, his fabric made him different from the rest of the product line. He was later replaced by the blue and black spotted Lizzy that is common today.

Tank the Armadillo #4031 is one of the few Beanies to have gone through two changes. First introduced in a longer style with a longer nose and seven lines across his back, Tank in gray had a third generation Ty tag. The next version showed us the same Tank, but now with nine lines sewn across his back and a fourth generation tag with a poem. Tank's current version is a smaller, more compact armadillo (about two inches shorter than the first) with a protective shell sewn on his back featuring nine lines stretching across it.

Stripes the Tiger (style #4065) in his first edition (commonly referred to by collectors as "Old Stripes") had a brown background to his body with black stripes about

The tie-dyed Lizzy was retired for cosmetic reasons. The plain version just looked better.

♥ 14 ♥

One of the rarest Beanie variations is the Quackers without wings.

one-quarter of an inch apart and a third generation tag. His replacement, also called Stripes, with the same product number, is more of a caramel color with stripes about one-half of an inch apart and a fourth generation tag with a poem. New Stripes was rumored heavily as a possible retirement candidate in May 1997 when a new tiger was introduced with the same body but a white background with black stripes. As we all know, Blizzard was an instant hit!

Smaller variations keep collectors searching for possible purchases and trades. Inch the Inchworm as we know him today (style #4044) is a multicolored worm in bright happy colors. His antennas on his head are made from yarn and he has a fourth generation tag with a poem. The original Inch has both a third and fourth generation tag, but what makes him special in the eyes of a collector is that his antennas were made from felt.

Another smaller variation involves Sly the Fox #4155. Just introduced in the Spring of 1996, his first shipments showed a Sly with a brown belly and a fourth generation tag. Rumor has it that dealers at a Beanie Baby convention held in Texas were asked their opinions of the new product line. Consensus ruled that Foxes should have white bellies. Management listened, and Sly had a white belly forevermore.

We can only close our eyes and imagine what changes might be in the works for the Beanie Babies line in the future. Only the main man, Mr. Ty Warner, knows for sure. . . . One thing remains certain, every little change will bc followed closely by his string of followers.

How to Collect Beanies

A Step-by-Step Guide to Landing the Collection of your Dreams

i t starts simply enough. A furtive glance. A soft caress. A brief hug. A bond is formed. You are infatuated with your new companion. You spend more time together, and, suddenly, you discover that you are in love. And you want more.

It's a testament to the allure of Beanie Babies that most people don't set out to build a collection. They initially buy one or two because they are inexpensive and "cute." They never realize they are taking the first step toward becoming a full-fledged, full-blown, full-time collector, but something about these understuffed, inexpensive animals keeps them going back for more. Like potato chips, they can't stop at just one.

Besides being inexpensive, Beanie Babies are an easy maintenance collectible. There is no box to save, nothing to break, and they require minimal room to display. Additionally, they appeal to both genders and all ages. It's easy for all members of the family to become involved in the collection. Boys, girls, moms, dads, and even grandparents collect Beanies.

Anne Nickels, Ty Inc. spokeswoman, agrees: "Grandparents — they're buying them for their grandchildren, and the next thing you know, they've got a collection of their own."

Getting Started

When starting a Beanie Babies collection, begin with buying those animals that attract you most. Not all styles

Have fun with your collection! Beanie Babies offer many possibilities. How about a circus?

by Vicky Krupka

of Beanies are considered adorable by everyone. Over time, most Beanie collectors have found that even the least attractive designs grow on them.

Take your time, don't worry about trying to buy everything all at once. Collectors find that the thrill of the chase — finding additions to their collection — is just as much fun as owning them. Remember, though, to proceed with caution. Give yourself time to learn about your new hobby. It can end up costing more if you rush into the secondary market too soon in pursuit of those "hard-to-find" Beanies.

A good place to begin your Beanie collection is by acquiring ones that tie in with an already existing collection. For example, a large number of adults collect bears. In the Beanie Babies Collection there are numerous different styles of bears: Valentino, Libearty, Peace, Garcia, Maple, Curly, Cubbie, Blackie, Chilly, Peking, and Teddy (in Brown, Cranberry, Jade, Magenta, Teal, and Violet). Many people, especially children, like to collect cats or dogs. These animals also have quite a representation in the Beanie Collection — domestic cats (Chip, Nip, Flip, and Zip), wild cats (Velvet, Stripes, Blizzard, Freckles and Roary), and dogs (Bernie, Bones, Doby, Dotty, Nanook, Pugsly, Rover, Scottie, Sparky, Spot, Tuffy, Weenie, and Wrinkles).

Display, or Play?

An important early step in putting together a collection is deciding if it will be for display only, for playing with, or a combination of both. This is important because the value of a Beanie directly relates to the condition of the Beanie itself and its tags.

Although you should be aware of the potential value of a collection, you should collect an item because you truly enjoy it and for the thrill of seeing a collection come together, not for its resale value.

If the Beanies are going to be played with, I would recommend removing the swing tags before giving them to children. The tag can be removed by sliding the plastic staple out through its insertion hole, saving both the tag and the staple. Tags and staples should be carefully stored away, ideally inside a Ziplock bag. Keeping them inside a sturdy box will help you to keep track of them and protect them. If done properly, the tag remains in mint condition and can be reinserted at a later time if desired.

Happy the Hunter

Finding a particular Beanie to add to your collection may require some work.

Unfortunately, retailers do not always know which Beanie they will receive at any one time. Checking stores regularly is your best bet. This also means checking more than one store, even if they are within walking distance of each other. Every retailer is on a different shipping schedule. With Ty deliberately creating an under-supply of Beanies,

you will need to keep in mind that shipments are not predictable.

Eye before Buy

Because there is considerable variation in the way Beanies of the same style are assembled, it is best to examine a Beanie closely before purchasing it. When given a choice, line up several of the same style. You will notice that each is sewn slightly differently, giving them individual personalities. Choose one with the most appeal. It is also recommended that Beanies be examined closely for manufacturing defects such as missing facial features, mis-sewn body parts, missing tags, open seams, etc.

Be sure to also examine both the swing (heart) and tush (sewn-in) tags. Make sure that the correct name for that animal appears on both tags. Beanies are mass-produced in China and Korea where English is not the primary language, and it is common to find Beanies with wrong tags on them and, occasionally, missing a swing or tush tag. Some people like to collect mistagged Beanies, while others try to sell them for more money, claiming these mistakes make them unique or rare. Presently, however, the consensus is that most mistagged, or untagged, Beanies are less than "mint," and therefore less desirable.

The serious collector of Beanie Babies needs to learn the different variations in swing and tush tags. To date, Beanies have been produced with four different swing tags and three different tush tags. The older the tag, the more value attached to the Beanie. The current swing tag was introduced in mid-1996 and has a yellow star on the front with the words "Beanie Original Baby" in it. On the inside a birthday and poem appear for that particular Beanie. Current tush tags are printed in red and have the Beanie's name imprinted on it. There are too many variations and combinations to detail in this short space, but interested collectors may find more information in the book "Beanie Mania" by Becky Phillips and Becky Estenssoro.

Cyberbabies

With the Beanie Boom now in full force, collectors no longer have to dart from specialty store to specialty store to acquire the whole line of cushy creatures. A quick Internet search on the keyword "Beanie" will find a wide assortment of retail stores that sell Beanies by mail-order. There is also a huge Beanie Baby secondary market on the Internet, providing a place for sellers to sell their hard-to-find Beanies, while enabling buyers the chance to complete their own collections without leaving their houses. A large number of sites offer space for people to post buy, sell and trade ads for current, hard-to-find, and retired Beanies.

Before buying through the secondary market, it is best to be well-informed about the Beanies you are searching out. You need to know if they are current or retired; if they were ever made in different designs or colors; which tags they have been produced with; and if they ever appeared with an "error" on them. Each of these factors greatly affects price.

If you are unsure about anything, there are many sites on the Internet that a collector can check for Beanie information. One of the first sites people check is Ty's website at www.Ty.com. Although Ty has updated its website, the pictures quite often are outdated. Be careful when using them to compare against recent purchases. In particular, Ty does not have updated pictures of several Beanies that have gone through design changes, and some pictures are just in error. For example, as recently as mid-June they still displayed pictures of the older retired versions of animals such as Stripes, Lucky and Tank. Additionally, the picture of Righty shows the flag on his right hip, but Righty was produced with the flag on his left hip, and the picture of Mel shows him as a brown koala bear, but he is gray.

When in doubt about an item, do not hesitate to tap the resources of the many Beanie experts available through the Internet. Two of the more well-known and popular sites that provide information are BeanieMom (www.beaniemom.com) and Kim's (www.knkcollectibles.com). Accessing "Teddie Bear's Ultimate Beanie Baby Resource" (www.geocities.com/EnchantedForest/9501) will also prove helpful, as it provides a comprehensive list of Beanie-related sites.

A growing source for buying retired or hard-to-find Beanies is flea markets, toy shows and swap meets. As Beanie Babies grow in popularity, so do the number of shows and events that cater to Beanie collectors. Be sure to look in local papers for such events. Be aware though, that most show sellers will accept only cash, and bargains are difficult to find. It is, however, worth a trip to see the many types of current and retired Beanies.

And who knows, you just might spot that lost love you've been seeking.

Two Beanies embroiled in controversy were Garcia and Chops. Rumor has it they were retired because of trademark issues with the Jerry Garcia estate and Shari Lewis of Lamb Chop fame.

Ally *the* Alligator

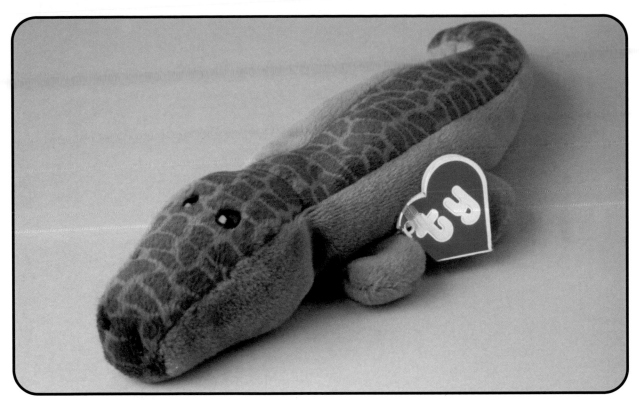

Item #:	4032
Issued:	1994
Retired:	10/97
Birthday:	3/14/94
Poem:	When Ally gets out of classes He wears a hat and dark glasses He plays bass in a street band He's the coolest gator in the land!

Baldy *the Eagle*

.... $6.00

Item #:	4074
Issued:	1997
Birthday:	2/17/96
Poem:	Hair on his head is quite scant
	We suggest Baldy get a transplant
	Watching over the land of the free
	Hair in his eyes would make it hard to see!

Batty the Bat

4th Generation

The Beanie Babies™ Collection

© Ty Inc.
Oakbrook IL. U.S.A.

© Ty UK Ltd.
Fareham, Hants
PO15 5TX

© Ty Deutschland
90008 Nürnberg

Handmade in China

[Beanie Name]™ [Style Number]

DATE OF BIRTH [Month-Day-Year]

[Beanie Poem]

Visit our web page!!!
http://www.ty.com

. . . . $10.

Item #:	4035
Issued:	1997
Birthday:	10/29/96
Poem:	Bats may make some people jitter
	Please don't be scared of this critter
	If you're lonely or have nothing to do
	This Beanie Baby would love to hug you!

Bernie *the St. Bernard*

.... $6.00

Item #:	4109
Issued:	1997
Birthday:	10/3/96
Poem:	This little dog can't wait to grow
	To rescue people lost in snow
	Don't let him out – keep him on your shelf
	He doesn't know how to rescue himself!

Bessie the Brown Cow

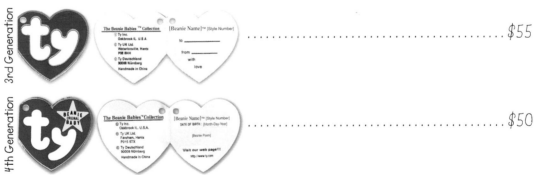
Item #:	4009
Issued:	1995
Retired:	10/97
Birthday:	6/27/95
Poem:	Bessie the cow likes to dance and sing
	Because music is her favorite thing
	Every night when you are counting sheep
	She'll sing you a song to help you sleep!

Blackie *the Black Bear*

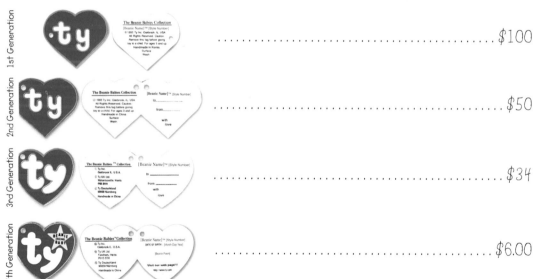

Item #:	4011
Issued:	1994
Birthday:	7/15/94
Poem:	Living in a national park
	He only played after dark
	Then he met his friend Cubbie
	Now they play when it's sunny!

Blizzard *the White Tiger*

4th Generation

The Beanie Babies™ Collection
® Ty Inc.
Oakbrook IL. U.S.A.
® Ty UK Ltd.
Fareham, Hants
PO15 5TX
® Ty Deutschland
90008 Nürnberg
Handmade in China

[Beanie Name]™ [Style Number]
DATE OF BIRTH [Month-Day-Year]

[Beanie Poem]

Visit our web page!!!
http://www.ty.com

.... $10

Item #:	4163
Issued:	1997
Birthday:	12/12/96
Poem:	In the mountains where it's snowy and cold
	Lives a beautiful tiger, I've been told
	Black and white, she's hard to compare
	Of all the tigers, she is the most rare.

Bones *the* Dog

Item #:	4001
Issued:	1995
Birthday:	1/18/94
Poem:	Bones is a dog that loves to chew
	Chairs and a table and a smelly old shoe
	"You're so destructive" all would shout
	But that all stopped when his teeth fell out!

Bongo the Monkey

Item #:	4067
Issued:	1995
Birthday:	8/17/95
Poem:	Bongo the Monkey lives in a tree The happiest monkey you'll ever see In his spare time he plays the guitar One of these days he will be a big star!

Bronty the Brontosaurus

The Beanie Babies ™ Collection

© Ty Inc.
Oakbrook IL. U.S.A.
© Ty UK Ltd.
Waterlooville, Hants
PO8 8HH
© Ty Deutschland
90008 Nürnberg
Handmade in China

[Beanie Name]™ [Style Number]

to _____

from _____
with
love

$900

Item #:	4085
Issued:	1995
Retired:	1996
Birthday:	Unknown
Poem:	None

Bubbles the Fish

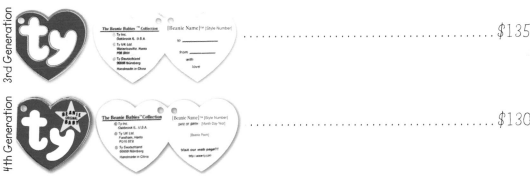

Item #:	4078
Issued:	1995
Retired:	5/97
Birthday:	7/2/95
Poem:	All day long Bubbles likes to swim She never gets tired of flapping her fins Bubbles lived in a sea of blue Now she is ready to come home with you!

Bucky the Beaver

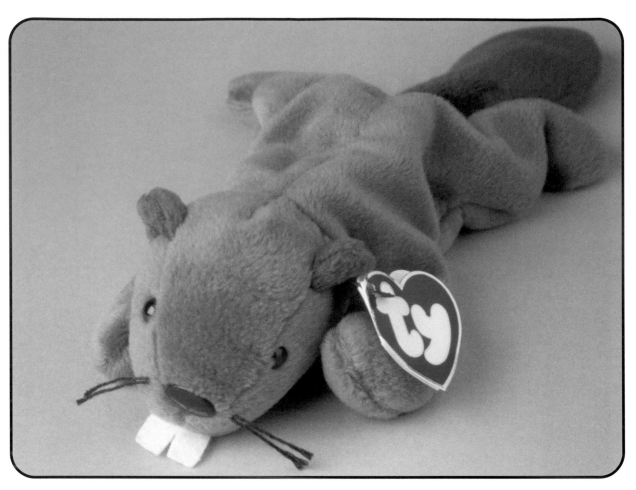

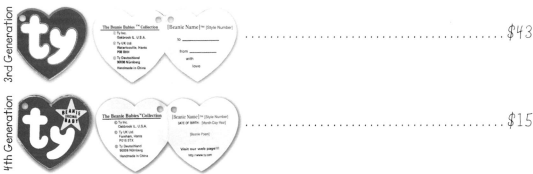

Item #:	4016
Issued:	1995
Retired:	1/98
Birthday:	6/8/95
Poem:	Bucky's teeth are as shiny as can be
	Often used for cutting trees
	He hides in his dam night and day
	Maybe for you he will come out and play!

Bumble the Bee

3rd Generation

The Beanie Babies™ Collection
Ⓒ Ty Inc.
Oakbrook IL. U.S.A.
Ⓒ Ty UK Ltd
Waterlooville, Hants
PO8 8NH
Ⓒ Ty Deutschland
90008 Nürnberg
Handmade in China

[Beanie Name]™ [Style Number]
to _____
from _____
with
love
.... $650

4th Generation

The Beanie Babies™ Collection
Ⓒ Ty Inc.
Oakbrook IL. U.S.A.
Ⓒ Ty UK Ltd
Fareham, Hants
PO15 5TX
Ⓒ Ty Deutschland
90008 Nürnberg
Handmade in China

[Beanie Name]™ [Style Number]
DATE OF BIRTH: [Month-Day-Year]

[Beanie Poem]

Visit our web page!!!
http://www.ty.com
.... $600

Item #:	4045
Issued:	1995
Retired:	1996
Birthday:	10/16/95
Poem:	Bumble the bee will not sting you
	It is only love that this bee will bring you
	So don't be afraid to give this bee a hug
	Because Bumble the bee is a love-bug.

The Beanie Babies ™ Collection

© Ty Inc.
Oakbrook IL. U.S.A.

© Ty UK Ltd.
Waterlooville, Hants
POB 8HH

© Ty Deutschland
90008 Nürnberg
Handmade in China

[Beanie Name]™ [Style Number]

to _____

from _____

with

love

. . . . $600

Item #:	4071
Issued:	1995
Retired:	1996
Birthday:	Unknown
Poem:	None

Chilly the Polar Bear

1st Generation

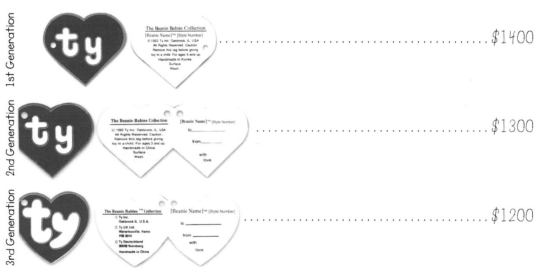

The Beanie Babies Collection
[Beanie Name]™ [Style Number]
© 1993 Ty Inc. Oakbrook, IL. USA
All Rights Reserved. Caution.
Remove this tag before giving
toy to a child. For ages 5 and up.
Handmade in Korea.
Surface
Wash.
....$1400

2nd Generation

The Beanie Babies Collection
© 1993 Ty Inc. Oakbrook, IL. USA
All Rights Reserved. Caution.
Remove this tag before giving
toy to a child. For ages 3 and up.
Handmade in China
Surface
Wash.

[Beanie Name]™ [Style Number]
to_____
from_____
with
love
....$1300

3rd Generation

The Beanie Babies ™ Collection
Ⓒ Ty Inc.
Oakbrook IL. U.S.A.
Ⓒ Ty UK Ltd.
Waterlooville, Hants
PO8 8HH
Ⓒ Ty Deutschland
90008 Nürnberg
Handmade in China

[Beanie Name]™ [Style Number]
to _____
from _____
with
love
....$1200

Item #:	4012
Issued:	1995
Retired:	1996
Birthday:	Unknown
Poem:	None

Chip the Calico Cat

4th Generation

The Beanie Babies™ Collection

℗ Ty Inc.
Oakbrook IL. U.S.A.

℗ Ty UK Ltd.
Fareham, Hants
PO15 5TX

℗ Ty Deutschland
90008 Nürnberg

Handmade in China

[Beanie Name]™ [Style Number]

DATE OF BIRTH [Month-Day-Year]

[Beanie Poem]

Visit our web page!!!

http://www.ty.com

.... $7.00

Item #:	4121
Issued:	1997
Birthday:	Unknown
Poem:	Black and gold, brown and white The shades of her coat are quite a sight At mixing her colors she was a master On anyone else it would be a disaster!

Chocolate the Moose

Item #:	4015
Issued:	1994
Birthday:	4/27/93
Poem:	Licorice, gum and peppermint candy
	This moose always has these handy
	But there is one more thing he likes to eat
	Can you guess his favorite sweet?

Chops the Lamb

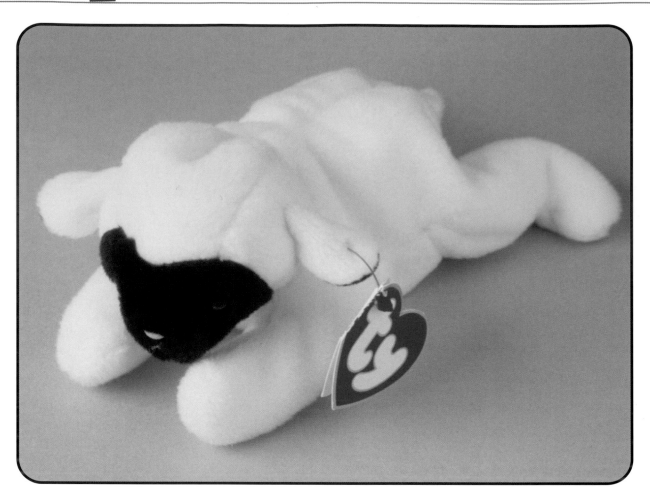

 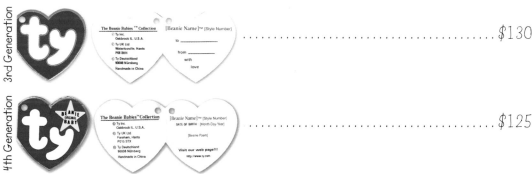
Item #:   4019

Issued: 1996

Retired: 1997

Poem: Chops is a little lamb
            This lamb you'll surely know
            Because every path that you may take
            This lamb is sure to go!

Claude *the* Crab

4th Generation

The Beanie Babies™ Collection

Ⓒ Ty Inc.
Oakbrook IL, U.S.A.

Ⓒ Ty UK Ltd.
Fareham, Hants
PO15 5TX

Ⓒ Ty Deutschland
90008 Nürnberg

Handmade in China

[Beanie Name]™ [Style Number]
DATE OF BIRTH: [Month-Day-Year]

[Beanie Poem]

Visit our web page!!!
http://www.ty.com

.... $8.00

Item #:	4083
Issued:	1997
Birthday:	9/3/96
Poem:	Claude the crab paints by the sea A famous artist he hopes to be But the tide came in and his paints fell Now his art is on his shell!

Congo *the* Gorilla

4th Generation

The Beanie Babies™ Collection
® Ty Inc.
  Oakbrook IL. U.S.A.
® Ty UK Ltd.
  Fareham, Hants
  PO15 STX
® Ty Deutschland
  90008 Nürnberg
  Handmade in China

[Beanie Name]™ [Style Number]
DATE OF BIRTH [Month-Day-Year]

[Beanie Poem]

Visit our web page!!!
http://www.ty.com

. . . . $5.50

Item #:	4160
Issued:	1996
Birthday:	11/9/96
Poem:	Black as night and fierce is he On the ground or in a tree Strong and mighty as the Congo He's related to our Bongo!

Coral the Fish

 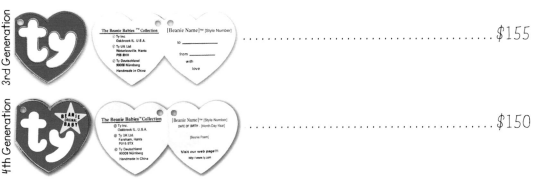
Item #:	4079
Issued:	1995
Retired:	1/97
Birthday:	3/2/95
Poem:	Coral is beautiful, as you know Made of colors in the rainbow Whether it's pink, yellow or blue These colors were chosen just for you!

Crunch the Shark

The Beanie Babies™ Collection

⊕ Ty Inc.
Oakbrook IL. U.S.A.

⊕ Ty UK Ltd.
Fareham, Hants
PO15 5TX

⊕ Ty Deutschland
90008 Nürnberg
Handmade in China

[Beanie Name] ™ [Style Number]

DATE OF BIRTH   [Month-Day-Year]

[Beanie Poem]

Visit our web page!!!
http://www.ty.com

.... $6.00

Item #:	4130
Issued:	1997
Birthday:	1/13/96
Poem:	What's for breakfast? What's for lunch?
	Yum? Delicious! Munch, munch, munch!
	He's eating everything by the bunch
	That's the reason we named him Crunch!

Cubbie *the Brown Bear*

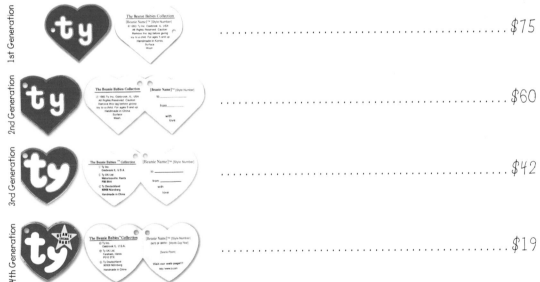

1st Generation		.... $75
2nd Generation		.... $60
3rd Generation		.... $42
4th Generation		.... $19

Item #:	4010
Issued:	1994
Retired:	1/98
Birthday:	11/14/93
Poem:	Cubbie used to eat crackers and honey
	And what happened to him was funny
	He was stung by fourteen bees
	Now Cubbie eats broccoli and cheese.

Curly *the Napped Bear*

4th Generation

The Beanie Babies™ Collection

© Ty Inc.
Oakbrook IL. U.S.A.

© Ty UK Ltd.
Fareham, Hants
PO15 5TX

© Ty Deutschland
90008 Nürnberg

Handmade in China

[Beanie Name]™ [Style Number]

DATE OF BIRTH: [Month-Day-Year]

[Beanie Poem]

Visit our web page!!!
http://www.ty.com

. . . . $10

Item #:	4052
Issued:	1996
Birthday:	4/12/96
Poem:	A bear so cute with hair that's curly You will love and want him surely To this bear always be true He will be a friend to you!

Daisy *the Black and White Cow*

 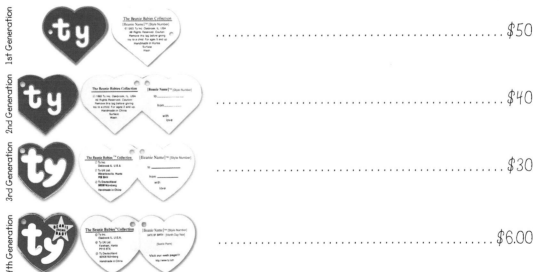
Item #:   4006

Issued: 1994

Birthday: 5/10/94

Poem: Daisy drinks milk each night
            So her coat is shiny and bright
            Milk is good for your hair and skin
            What a way for your day to begin!

Derby the Horse

3rd Generation

The Beanie Babies™ Collection

© Ty Inc.
Oakbrook IL. U.S.A.
Ty UK Ltd.
Waterlooville, Hants
PO8 8HH
Ty Deutschland
90008 Nürnberg
Handmade in China

[Beanie Name]™ [Style Number]

to _____

from _____

with

love

Fine Yarn Mane. $1200
Coarse Yarn Mane $50

4th Generation

The Beanie Babies™ Collection

© Ty Inc.
Oakbrook IL. U.S.A.
© Ty UK Ltd.
Fareham, Hants
PO15 5TX
© Ty Deutschland
90008 Nürnberg
Handmade in China

[Beanie Name]™ [Style Number]
DATE OF BIRTH   [Month-Day-Year]

[Beanie Poem]

Visit our web page!!!
http://www.ty.com

Coarse Yarn Mane. $8.00
"Star," Coarse Mane. $6.00

Item #:	4008
Issued:	1995
Birthday:	9/16/95
Poem:	All the other horses used to tattle
	Because Derby never wore his saddle
	He left the stables, and the horses too
	Just so Derby can be with you!

Digger *the* Crab

Old - Orange   New - Red

1st Generation

Orange...................................$500

2nd Generation

Orange...................................$450

3rd Generation

Orange...................................$400
Red......................................$100

4th Generation

Red......................................$100

Item #:	4027
Issued:	1995
Retired:	5/97
Birthday:	8/23/95
Poem:	Digging in the sand and walking sideways
	That's how Digger spends her days
	Hard on the outside but sweet deep inside
	Basking in the sun, riding the tide!

Doby the Doberman

The Beanie Babies™ Collection
© Ty Inc.
Oakbrook IL. U.S.A.
© Ty UK Ltd.
Fareham, Hants
PO15 5TX
© Ty Deutschland
90008 Nürnberg
Handmade in China

[Beanie Name]™ [Style Number]
DATE OF BIRTH   [Month-Day-Year]

[Beanie Poem]

Visit our web page!!!
http://www.ty.com

.... $5.50

Item #:	4110
Issued:	1997
Birthday:	10/9/96
Poem:	This dog is little but he has might Keep him close when you sleep at night He lays around with nothing to do Until he sees it's time to protect you!

Doodle *the* Rooster

4th Generation

The Beanie Babies™ Collection

© Ty Inc.
Oakbrook IL. U.S.A.
© Ty UK Ltd.
Fareham, Hants
PO15 5TX
© Ty Deutschland
90008 Nürnberg
Handmade in China

[Beanie Name]™ [Style Number]
DATE OF BIRTH: [Month-Day-Year]

[Beanie Poem]

Visit our web page!!!
http://www.ty.com

....$40

Item #:	4171
Issued:	1997
Birthday:	3/8/96
Poem:	Listen closely to "Cock-a-doodle-doo"
	What's the rooster saying to you?
	Hurry, wake up sleepy head
	We have lots to do, get out of bed!

Dotty the Dalmation

4th Generation

$5.50

Item #:	4100
Issued:	1997
Birthday:	10/17/96
Poem:	The Beanies all thought it was a big joke
	While writing her tag, their ink pen broke
	She got in the way, and got all spotty
	So now the Beanies call her Dotty!

Ears the Rabbit

3rd Generation

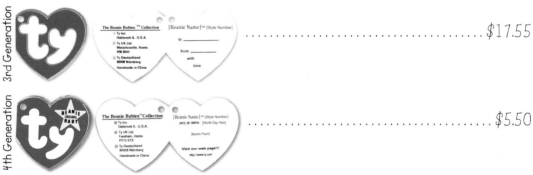

The Beanie Babies ™ Collection

© Ty Inc.
Oakbrook IL. U.S.A.
© Ty UK Ltd
Waterlooville, Hants
POE 8HH
© Ty Deutschland
90008 Nürnberg

Handmade in China

[Beanie Name]™ [Style Number]

to _____
from _____
with
love

. . . . $17.55

4th Generation

The Beanie Babies™ Collection

© Ty Inc.
Oakbrook IL. U.S.A.
© Ty UK Ltd
Fareham, Hants
PO15 5TX
© Ty Deutschland
90008 Nürnberg

Handmade in China

[Beanie Name]™ [Style Number]

DATE OF BIRTH : [Month-Day-Year]

[Beanie Poem]

Visit our web page!!!
http://www.ty.com

. . . . $5.50

Item #:	4018
Issued:	1996
Birthday:	4/18/95
Poem:	He's been eating carrots so long Didn't understand what was wrong Couldn't see the board during classes Until the doctor gave him glasses!

Echo the Dolphin

4th Generation

The Beanie Babies™ Collection
® Ty Inc.
Oakbrook IL, U.S.A.
® Ty UK Ltd.
Fareham, Hants
PO15 5TX
® Ty Deutschland
90008 Nürnberg
Handmade in China

[Beanie Name]™ [Style Number]
DATE OF BIRTH [Month-Day-Year]

[Beanie Poem]

Visit our web page!!!
http://www.ty.com

. . . . $5.50

Item #:	4180
Issued:	1997
Birthday:	12/21/96
Poem:	Echo the dolphin lives in the sea Playing with her friends, like you and me Through the waves she echoes the sound "I'm so glad to have you around!"

Flash the Dolphin

1st Generation		.... $120
2nd Generation		.... $110
3rd Generation		.... $100
4th Generation		.... $100

Item #:   4021
Issued: 1994
Retired: 5/97
Birthday: 5/13/93
Poem: You know dolphins are a smart breed
             Our friend flash knows how to read
             Splash the whale is the one who taught her
             Although reading is difficult under the water.

Fleece the Lamb

4th Generation

The Beanie Babies™Collection

® Ty Inc.
Oakbrook IL, U.S.A.

® Ty UK Ltd.
Fareham, Hants
PO15 5TX

® Ty Deutschland
90008 Nürnberg

Handmade in China

[Beanie Name]™ [Style Number]

DATE OF BIRTH: [Month-Day-Year]

[Beanie Poem]

Visit our web page!!!
http://www.ty.com

$6.00

Item #:	4125
Issued:	1997
Birthday:	3/21/96
Poem:	Fleece would like to sing a lullaby
	Please be patient, she's really shy
	When you sleep, keep her by your ear
	Her song will leave you nothing to fear.

Flip the Cat

Item #:	4012
Issued:	1996
Retired:	10/97
Birthday:	2/28/95
Poem:	Flip the cat is an acrobat She loves playing on her mat This cat flips with such grace and flair She can somersault in midair.

Floppity *the Lavender Bunny*

. . . . $7.00

Item #:	4118
Issued:	1997
Birthday:	5/28/96
Poem:	Floppity hops from here to there
	Searching for eggs without a care
	Lavender coat from head to toe
	All dressed up and nowhere to go!

ꟻlutter *the* Butterfly

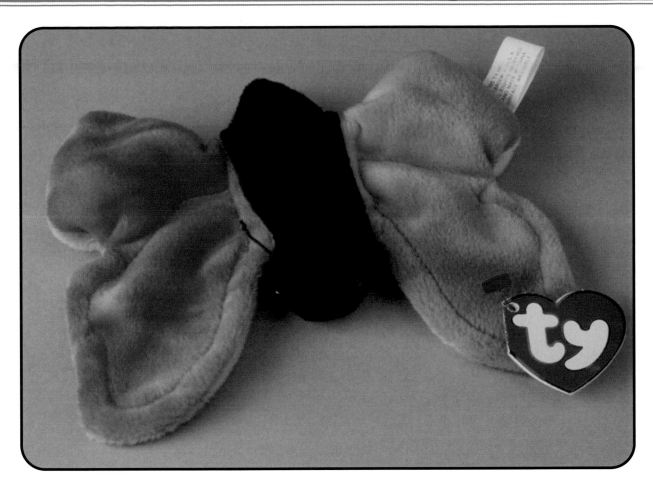

3rd Generation

The Beanie Babies ™ Collection   [Beanie Name]™ [Style Number]

© Ty Inc.
Oakbrook IL. U.S.A.

® Ty UK Ltd.
Waterlooville, Hants
P08 8HH

© Ty Deutschland
90008 Nürnberg
Handmade in China

to _____

from _____

with

love

....$800

Item #:	4043
Issued:	1995
Retired:	1996
Birthday:	Unknown
Poem:	None

Freckles the Leopard

4th Generation

ty
BEANIE ORIGINAL BABY

The Beanie Babies™ Collection

Ⓖ Ty Inc.
Oakbrook IL. U.S.A.

Ⓒ Ty UK Ltd.
Fareham, Hants
PO15 5TX

Ⓒ Ty Deutschland
90008 Nürnberg

Handmade in China

[Beanie Name]™ [Style Number]

DATE OF BIRTH: [Month-Day-Year]

[Beanie Poem]

Visit our web page!!!
http://www.ty.com

. . . . $6.75

Item #:	4066
Issued:	1996
Birthday:	6/3/96
Poem:	From the trees he hunts his prey In the night and in the day He's the king of camouflage Look real close, he's no mirage!

Garcia *the* Bear

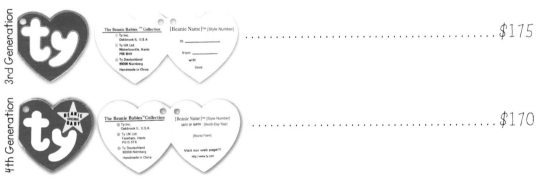

3rd Generation $175

4th Generation $170

Item #:	4051
Issued:	1995
Retired:	5/97
Birthday:	8/1/95
Poem:	The Beanies used to follow him around
	Because Garcia traveled from town to town
	He's pretty popular as you can see
	Some even say he's legendary.

Gobbles the Turkey

4th Generation

The Beanie Babies™ Collection

® Ty Inc.
Oakbrook IL. U.S.A.

® Ty UK Ltd.
Fareham, Hants
PO15 5TX

® Ty Deutschland
90008 Nürnberg
Handmade in China

[Beanie Name] ™ [Style Number]

DATE OF BIRTH [Month-Day-Year]

[Beanie Poem]

Visit our web page!!!
http://www.ty.com

. . . . $10

Item #:	4034
Issued:	1997
Birthday:	11/27/96
Poem:	Gobbles the turkey loves to eat
	Once a year she has a feast
	I have a secret I'd like to divulge
	If she eats too much her tummy will bulge!

Goldie *the* Goldfish

....$60

....$55

....$50

....$35

Item #:	4023
Issued:	1994
Retired:	1/98
Birthday:	11/14/94
Poem:	She's got rhythm, she's got soul
	What more to like in a fish bowl?
	Through sound waves Goldie swam
	Because this goldfish likes to jam!

Gracie the Swan

The Beanie Babies™ Collection

® Ty Inc.
Oakbrook IL, U.S.A.
® Ty UK Ltd.
Fareham, Hants
PO15 5TX
® Ty Deutschland
90008 Nürnberg
Handmade in China

[Beanie Name]™ [Style Number]
DATE OF BIRTH: [Month-Day-Year]

[Beanie Poem]

Visit our web page!!!
http://www.ty.com

.... $6.25

Item #:	4126
Issued:	1997
Birthday:	6/17/96
Poem:	As a duckling, she was confused Birds on the lake were quite amused Poking fun until she would cry, Now the most beautiful swan at Ty!

Grunt the Razorback

Item #:	4092
Issued:	1995
Retired:	5/97
Birthday:	7/19/95
Poem:	Some Beanies think Grunt is tough
	No surprise, he's scary enough
	But if you take him home you'll see
	Grunt is the sweetest Beanie Baby!

Happy the Hippo

Old - Gray

New - Lavender

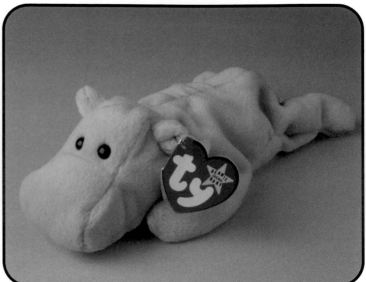

1st Generation

Gray......................................$450

2nd Generation

Gray......................................$425

3rd Generation

Gray......................................$400
Lavender $15.00

4th Generation

Lavender.................................$6.00

Item #:	4061
Issued:	1994
Birthday:	2/25/94
Poem:	Happy the hippo loves to wade In the river and in the shade When Happy shoots water out of his snout You know he's happy without a doubt!

♥ 62 ♥

Hippity *the Mint Bunny*

4th Generation

The Beanie Babies™ Collection
© Ty Inc.
Oakbrook IL. U.S.A.
© Ty UK Ltd.
Fareham, Hants
PO15 5TX
© Ty Deutschland
90008 Nürnberg
Handmade in China

[Beanie Name] [™ [Style Number]
DATE OF BIRTH: [Month-Day-Year]

[Beanie Poem]

Visit our web page!!!
http://www.ty.com

.... $7.00

Item #:	4119
Issued:	1997
Birthday:	6/1/96
Poem:	Hippity is a cute little bunny
	Dressed in green, he looks quite funny
	Twitching his nose in the air
	Sniffing a flower here and there!

Hoot the Owl

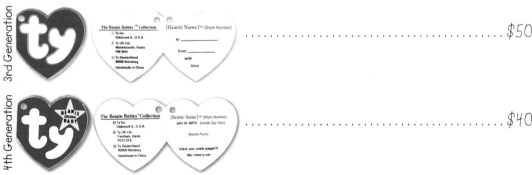

3rd Generation

The Beanie Babies™ Collection   [Beanie Name]™ [Style Number]
ⓐ Ty Inc.
  Oakbrook IL. U.S.A.   to _____
ⓑ Ty UK Ltd.
  Waterlooville, Hants   from _____
  PO8 8HH
                              with
ⓒ Ty Deutschland
  90008 Nürnberg   love
  Handmade in China
                                    . . . . $50

4th Generation

The Beanie Babies™Collection   [Beanie Name]™ [Style Number]
ⓐ Ty Inc.   DATE OF BIRTH: [Month-Day-Year]
  Oakbrook IL. U.S.A.
ⓑ Ty UK Ltd.   [Beanie Poem]
  Fareham, Hants
  PO15 5TX
ⓒ Ty Deutschland   Visit our web page!!!
  90008 Nürnberg   http //www ty com
  Handmade in China
                                    . . . . $40

Item #:	4073
Issued:	1995
Retired:	10/97
Birthday:	8/9/95
Poem:	Late to bed, late to rise
	Nevertheless, Hoot's quite wise
	Studies by candlelight, nothing new
	Like a president, do you know who?

Hoppity the Pink Bunny

4th Generation

The Beanie Babies™ Collection

® Ty Inc.
Oakbrook IL, U.S.A.

® Ty UK Ltd.
Fareham, Hants
PO15 5TX

® Ty Deutschland
90008 Nürnberg

Handmade in China

[Beanie Name]™ [Style Number]

DATE OF BIRTH: [Month-Day-Year]

[Beanie Poem]

Visit our web page!!!
http://www.ty.com

....$7.00

Item #:	4117
Issued:	1997
Birthday:	4/3/96
Poem:	Hopscotch is what she likes to play
	If you don't join in, she'll hop away
	So play a game if you have the time
	She likes to play, rain or shine.

Humphrey the Camel

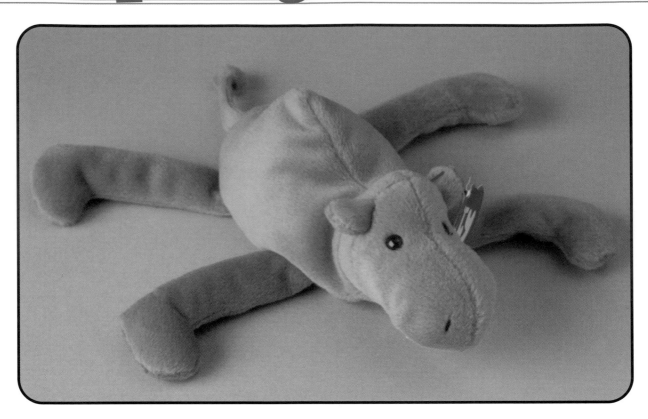

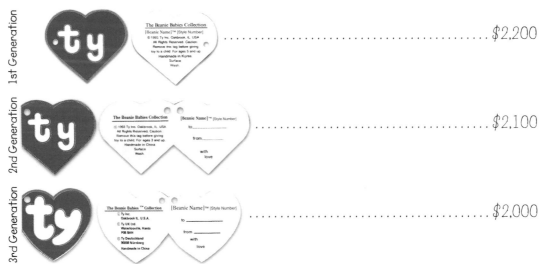

Item #:	4060
Issued:	1994
Retired:	1996
Birthday:	Unknown
Poem:	None

Inch the Worm

3rd Generation

The Beanie Babies™ Collection
Ⓒ Ty Inc.
   Oakbrook IL. U.S.A.
Ⓒ Ty UK Ltd.
   Waterlooville, Hants
   P08 8HH
Ⓒ Ty Deutschland
   90008 Nürnberg
Handmade in China

[Beanie Name]™ [Style Number]
to _____
from _____
with
love

Felt antennae..........................$130

4th Generation

The Beanie Babies™ Collection
Ⓒ Ty Inc.
   Oakbrook IL. U.S.A.
Ⓒ Ty UK Ltd.
   Fareham, Hants
   P015 5TX
Ⓒ Ty Deutschland
   90008 Nürnberg
Handmade in China

[Beanie Name]™ [Style Number]
DATE OF BIRTH: [Month-Day-Year]
[Beanie Poem]
Visit our web page!!!
http://www.ty.com

Felt antennae.........................$67.50
Yarn antennae $5.50

Item #:	4044
Issued:	1995
Birthday:	9/3/95
Poem:	Inch the worm is a friend of mine He goes so slow all the time Inching around from here to there Traveling the world without a care.

Inky *the Octopus*

Old - Tan

New - Pink

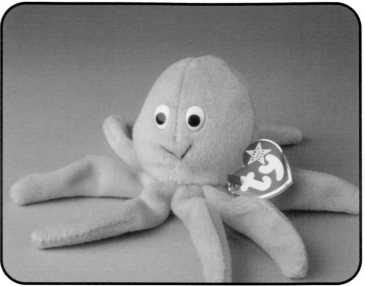

 **1st Generation** Tan, No Mouth............................$300

 **2nd Generation** Tan, No Mouth............................$300

 **3rd Generation** Tan.......................................$250
Pink....................................$17.50

4th Generation Pink.......................................$5.50

Item #:   4028

Issued: 1994

Birthday: 11/29/94

Poem: Inky's head is big and round
            As he swims he makes no sound
            If you need a hand, don't hesitate
            Inky can help because he has eight!

Jolly the Walrus

4th Generation

The Beanie Babies™ Collection

℗ Ty Inc.
Oakbrook IL, U.S.A.

℗ Ty UK Ltd.
Fareham, Hants
PO15 5TX

℗ Ty Deutschland
90008 Nürnberg

Handmade in China

[Beanie Name]™ [Style Number]

DATE OF BIRTH : [Month-Day-Year]

[Beanie Poem]

Visit our web page!!!
http://www.ty.com

.... $7.00

Item #:	4082
Issued:	1997
Birthday:	12/2/96
Poem:	Jolly the walrus is not very serious
	He laughs and laughs until he's delirious
	He often reminds me of my dad
	Always happy, never sad!

Kiwi *the* Toucan

3rd Generation $160

4th Generation $150

Item #:	4070
Issued:	1995
Retired:	5/97
Birthday:	9/16/95
Poem:	Kiwi waits for April showers
	Watching a garden bloom with flowers
	There trees grow with fruit that's sweet
	I'm sure you'll guess his favorite treat!

Lefty the Donkey

4th Generation

The Beanie Babies™ Collection

Ⓡ Ty Inc.
Oakbrook IL, U.S.A.

Ⓡ Ty UK Ltd.
Fareham, Hants
PO15 5TX

Ⓡ Ty Deutschland
50008 Nürnberg

Handmade in China

[Beanie Name]™ [Style Number]

DATE OF BIRTH [Month-Day-Year]

[Beanie Poem]

Visit our web page!!!
http://www.ty.com

.... $280

Item #:	4057
Issued:	1996
Retired:	1/97
Birthday:	7/4/96
Poem:	Donkeys to the left, elephants to the right
	Often seems like a crazy sight
	This whole game seems very funny
	Until you realize they're spending your money!

Legs the Frog

1st Generation $50

2nd Generation $35

3rd Generation $30

4th Generation $25

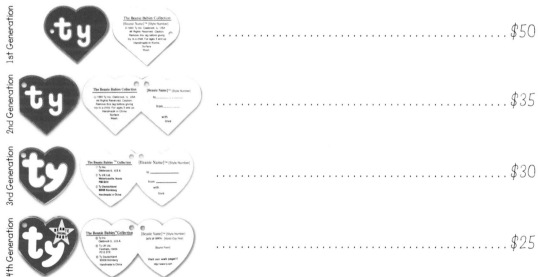

Item #:	4020
Issued:	1994
Retired:	10/97
Birthday:	4/25/93
Poem:	Legs lives in a hollow log
	Legs likes to play leap frog
	If you like to hang out at the lake
	Legs will be the new friend you make!

Libearty *the* Bear

4th Generation

The Beanie Babies™ Collection

Ⓡ Ty Inc.
Oakbrook IL, U.S.A.
Ⓡ Ty UK Ltd.
Fareham, Hants
PO15 5TX
Ⓡ Ty Deutschland
50008 Nürnberg

Handmade in China

[Beanie Name]™ [Style Number]
DATE OF BIRTH : [Month-Day-Year]

[Beanie Poem]

Visit our web page!!!
http://www.ty.com

w/out Flag $450
w/Flag $350
w/Flag, "Beanine" Tag $350

Item #:	4057
Issued:	1996
Retired:	1996
Birthday:	Unknown
Poem:	I am called Libearty
	I wear the flag for all to see
	Hope and freedom is my way
	That's why I wear flag USA.

Lizzy the Lizard

Old - Tie-dyed

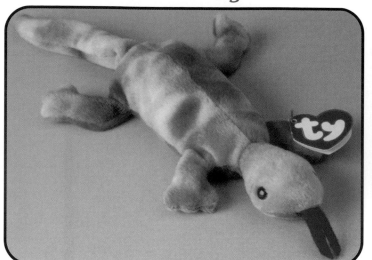

New - Blue & Yellow

3rd Generation

Tie-dyed............................$700
Blue & Yellow $40

4th Generation

Blue & Yellow $6.25

Item #:	4033
Issued:	1995
Retired:	1/98
Birthday:	5/11/95
Poem:	Lizzy loves Legs the frog
	She hides with him under logs
	Both of them search for flies
	Underneath the clear blue skies!

Lucky the Ladybug

Old - 7 Glued Dots

New - Large & Small Dots

1st Generation — Glued spots.............................$100

2nd Generation — Glued spots.............................$80

3rd Generation — Glued spots.............................$75

4th Generation — Small spaces $7.00
Large spaces..............................$7.00

Item #:	4040
Issued:	1994
Birthday:	5/1/95
Poem:	Lucky the lady bug loves the lotto
	"Someone must win" that's her motto
	But save your dimes and even a penny
	Don't spend on the lotto and you'll have many!

Magic *the* Dragon

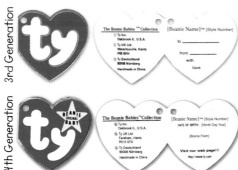

Light stitching.................$65

Light stitching.................$40
Hot pink stitching............$200

Item #:	4088
Issued:	1995
Retired:	1/98
Birthday:	9/5/95
Poem:	Magic the dragon lives in a dream
	The most beautiful that you have ever seen
	Through magic lands she likes to fly
	Look up and watch her, way up high!

Manny *the* Manatee

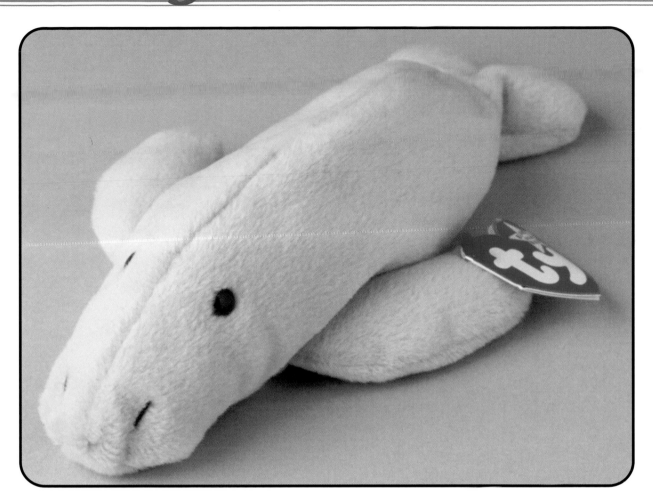

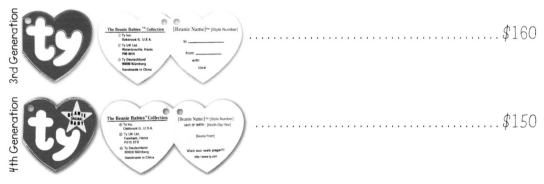
Item #:	4081
Issued:	1995
Retired:	5/97
Birthday:	6/8/95
Poem:	Manny is sometimes called a sea cow She likes to twirl and likes to bow Manny sure is glad you bought her Because it's so lonely underwater!

4th Generation

The Beanie Babies™ Collection

© Ty Inc.
Oakbrook IL, U.S.A.
© Ty UK Ltd.
Fareham, Hants
P015 5TX
© Ty Deutschland
90008 Nürnberg
Handmade in China

[Beanie Name]™ [Style Number]
DATE OF BIRTH: [Month-Day-Year]

[Beanie Poem]

Visit our web page!!!
http://www.ty.com

"Pride" tag $300
.... $180

Item #:	4600
Issued:	1996
Birthday:	7/1/96
Poem:	Maple the bear likes to ski With his friends, he plays hockey. He loves his pancakes and eats every crumb Can you guess which country he's from?

Mel *the* Koala Bear

The Beanie Babies™ Collection

© Ty Inc.
Oakbrook IL, U.S.A.

© Ty UK Ltd.
Fareham, Hants
PO15 STX

© Ty Deutschland
90008 Nürnberg
Handmade in China

[Beanie Name]™ [Style Number]

DATE OF BIRTH: [Month-Day-Year]

[Beanie Poem]

Visit our web page!!!
http://www.ty.com

....$6.00

Item #:	4162
Issued:	1997
Birthday:	1/15/96
Poem:	How do you name a Koala bear?
	It's rather tough, I do declare!
	It confuses me, I get in a funk
	I'll name him Mel, after my favorite hunk!

Mystic the Unicorn

1st Generation — Fine yarn mane $150

2nd Generation — Fine yarn mane $125

3rd Generation
Fine yarn mane $117
Coarse yarn mane $17.50

4th Generation
Coarse yarn, Old horn $30.00
Coarse yarn, New horn $15.00

Item #:	4007
Issued:	1994
Birthday:	5/21/94
Poem:	Once upon a time so far away
	A unicorn was born one day in May
	Keep Mystic with you, she's a prize
	You'll see the magic in her blue eyes!

Nanook the Husky

 4th Generation

The Beanie Babies™ Collection

® Ty Inc.
Oakbrook IL, U.S.A.

® Ty UK Ltd
Fareham, Hants
PO15 5TX

® Ty Deutschland
90008 Nürnberg

Handmade in China

[Beanie Name]™ [Style Number]

DATE OF BIRTH: [Month-Day-Year]

[Beanie Poem]

Visit our web page!!!
http://www.ty.com

. . . . $12.00

Item #:	4104
Issued:	1997
Birthday:	11/21/96
Poem:	Nanook is a dog that loves cold weather To him a sled is light as a feather Over the snow and through the slush He runs at hearing the cry of "mush!"

Nip *the Gold Cat*

Old - Gold w/White Face & Belly

Old - All Gold

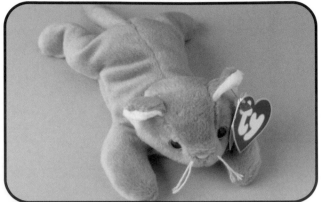

New - Gold w/White Paws

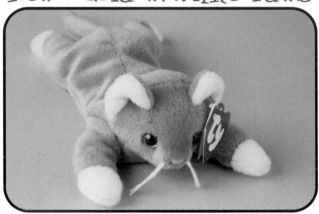

2nd Generation	White face & belly	$195
3rd Generation	White face & belly	$195
	All gold.	$530
	White paws.	$31.50
4th Generation	White paws.	$20.00

Item #:	4003
Issued:	1994
Retired:	1/98
Birthday:	3/6/94
Poem:	His name is Nipper, but we call him Nip
	His best friend is a black cat named Zip
	Nip likes to run in races for fun
	He runs so fast he's always number one!

Nuts the Squirrel

4th Generation

The Beanie Babies™ Collection

Ty Inc.
Oakbrook IL, U.S.A.

Ty UK Ltd
Fareham, Hants
PO15 5TX

Ty Deutschland
90008 Nürnberg

Handmade in China

[Beanie Name]™ [Style Number]
DATE OF BIRTH [Month-Day-Year]

[Beanie Poem]

Visit our web page!!!
http://www.ty.com

$6.00

Item #:	4114
Issued:	1997
Birthday:	1/21/96
Poem:	With his bushy tail, he'll scamper up a tree
	The most cheerful critter you'll ever see.
	He's nuts about nuts, and he loves to chat
	Have you ever seen a squirrel like that?

♥ 83 ♥

Patti the Platypus

1st Generation	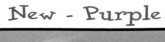	Maroon $600
2nd Generation		Maroon $575
3rd Generation		Maroon .... $575 Purple $40
4th Generation		Purple $6.00

Item #:   4025

Issued: 1994

Birthday: 1/6/93

Poem: Ran into Patti one day while walking
         Believe me she wouldn't stop talking!
         Listened and listened to her speak
         That would explain her extra large beak!

Peace *the* Tie-dye Bear

4th Generation

The Beanie Babies™ Collection
Ⓣ Ty Inc.
Oakbrook IL, U.S.A.
Ⓣ Ty UK Ltd.
Fareham, Hants
PO15 5TX
Ⓣ Ty Deutschland
90008 Nürnberg
Handmade in China

[Beanie Name]™ [Style Number]
DATE OF BIRTH: [Month-Day-Year]

[Beanie Poem]

Visit our web page!!!
http://www.ty.com

.... $40

Item #:	4053
Issued:	1997
Birthday:	2/1/96
Poem:	All races all colors, under the sun Join hands together and have some fun Dance to the music, rock and roll is the sound Symbols of peace and love abound!

Peanut the Elephant

Old - Royal Blue	New - Light Blue

 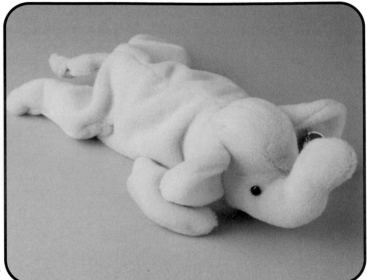

3rd Generation

The Beanie Babies™ Collection

ⓒ Ty Inc.
Oakbrook IL. U.S.A.

ⓤ Ty UK Ltd.
Waterlooville, Hants
P08 8HH

ⓖ Ty Deutschland
90008 Nürnberg

Handmade in China

[Beanie Name]™ [Style Number]

to _____

from _____
with
love

Royal Blue..............................$3,500
Light Blue...............................$20

4th Generation

The Beanie Babies™ Collection

ⓒ Ty Inc.
Oakbrook IL. U.S.A.

ⓤ Ty UK Ltd.
Fareham, Hants
P015 5TX

ⓖ Ty Deutschland
90008 Nürnberg

Handmade in China

[Beanie Name]™ [Style Number]
DATE OF BIRTH : [Month-Day-Year]

[Beanie Poem]

Visit our web page!!!
http://www.ty.com

Light Blue $6.00

Item #:	4062
Issued:	1995
Birthday:	1/25/95
Poem:	Peanut the elephant walks on tip-toes Quietly sneaking wherever she goes She'll sneak up on you and a hug you will get Peanuts is a friend you won't soon forget.

Peking *the* Panda Bear

1st Generation

The Beanie Babies Collection
[Beanie Name]™ [Style Number]
©1993 Ty Inc. Oakbrook, IL. USA
All Rights Reserved. Caution:
Remove this tag before giving
toy to a child. For ages 5 and up.
Handmade in Korea.
Surface
Wash

. . . . $1,100

2nd Generation

The Beanie Babies Collection
© 1993 Ty Inc. Oakbrook, IL. USA :
Remove this tag before giving
toy to a child. For ages 3 and up.
Handmade in China.
Surface
Wash.

[Beanie Name]™ [Style Number]
to _____
from _____
with
love

. . . . $1,100

3rd Generation

The Beanie Babies ™ Collection
© Ty Inc.
   Oakbrook IL. U.S.A.
© Ty UK Ltd.
   Waterlooville, Hants
   P08 8HH
© Ty Deutschland
   90008 Nürnberg
Handmade in China

[Beanie Name]™ [Style Number]
to _____
from _____
with
love

. . . . $1,100

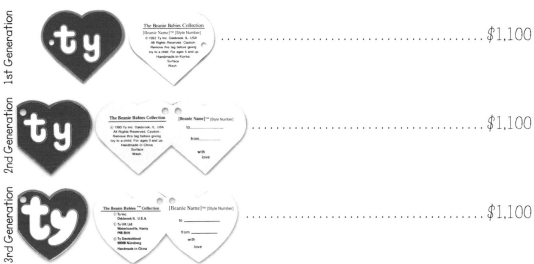

Item #:	4013
Issued:	1994
Retired:	1996
Birthday:	Unknown
Poem:	None

Pinchers the Lobster

 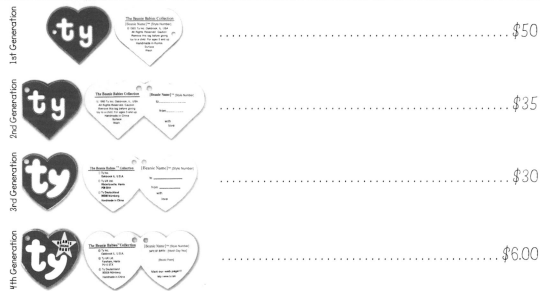
Item #:   4026

Issued: 1994

Birthday: 6/19/93

Poem: This lobster loves to pinch
            Eating his food inch by inch
            Balancing carefully with his tail
            Moving forward slow as a snail!

Pinky *the* Flamingo

3rd Generation

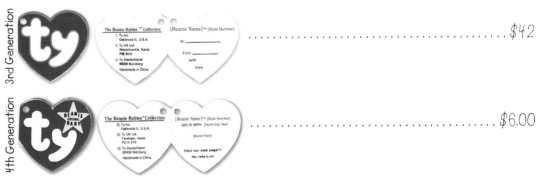

The Beanie Babies ™ Collection
Ⓒ Ty Inc.
Oakbrook IL. U.S.A.
Ⓒ Ty UK Ltd.
Waterlooville, Hants
PO8 8HH
Ⓒ Ty Deutschland
90008 Nürnberg
Handmade in China

[Beanie Name]™ [Style Number]

to _____

from _____
with
love

....$42

4th Generation

The Beanie Babies™ Collection
Ⓒ Ty Inc.
Oakbrook IL. U.S.A.
Ⓒ Ty UK Ltd.
Fareham, Hants
PO15 5TX
Ⓒ Ty Deutschland
90008 Nürnberg
Handmade in China

[Beanie Name]™ [Style Number]
DATE OF BIRTH: [Month-Day-Year]

[Beanie Poem]

Visit our web page!!!
http://www.ty.com

....$6.00

Item #:	4072
Issued:	1995
Birthday:	2/13/95
Poem:	Pinky loves the Everglades From the hottest pink she's made With floppy legs and big orange beak She's the Beanie that you seek!

Pouch *the* Kangaroo

4th Generation

The Beanie Babies™ Collection

℗ Ty Inc.
Oakbrook IL, U.S.A.

℗ Ty UK Ltd.
Fareham, Hants
PO15 5TX

℗ Ty Deutschland
90008 Nürnberg

Handmade in China

[Beanie Name]™ [Style Number]

DATE OF BIRTH : [Month-Day-Year]

[Beanie Poem]

Visit our web page!!!
http://www.ty.com

.... $6.00

Item #:	4161
Issued:	1997
Birthday:	11/6/96
Poem:	My little pouch is handy I've found It helps me carry my baby around I hop up and down without any fear Knowing my baby is safe and near.

Princess Bear

4th Generation

The Beanie Babies™ Collection
℗ Ty Inc.
Oakbrook IL. U.S.A.
℗ Ty UK Ltd.
Fareham, Hants
PO15 STX
℗ Ty Deutschland
90008 Nürnberg
Handmade in China

[Beanie Name]™ [Style Number]
DATE OF BIRTH : [Month-Day-Year]

[Beanie Poem]

Visit our web page!!!
http://www.ty.com

.... $350

Item #:	n/a
Issued:	1997
Birthday:	n/a
Poem:	Like an angel, she came from heaven above
	She shared her compassion, her pain, her love
	She only stayed with us long enough to teach
	The world to share, to give, to reach.

Pugsly *the Pug Dog*

The Beanie Babies™ Collection

® Ty Inc.
Oakbrook IL, U.S.A.
® Ty UK Ltd.
Fareham, Hants
P015 5TX
® Ty Deutschland
90008 Nürnberg
Handmade in China.

[Beanie Name]™ [Style Number]
DATE OF BIRTH [Month-Day-Year]

[Beanie Poem]

Visit our web page!!!
http://www.ty.com

. . . . $8.00

Item #:	4106
Issued:	1997
Birthday:	5/2/96
Poem:	Pugsly is picky about what he will wear Never a spot, a stain or a tear Image is something of which he'll gloat Until he noticed his wrinkled coat!

Quackers *the Duck*

Old - Without Wings
New - With Wings

1st Generation		without wings $1,500
2nd Generation		without wings ....$1,100 with wings $50
3rd Generation		with wings $40
4th Generation		with wings....................................$6.00

Item #:   4024

Issued: 1994

Birthday: 4/19/94

Poem: There is a duck by the name of Quackers
             Every night he eats animal crackers
             He swims in a lake that's clear and blue
             But he'll come to the shore to be with you!

Radar *the* Bat

<table>
</table>

3rd Generation

The Beanie Babies™ Collection
© Ty Inc.
Oakbrook Il, U.S.A.
© Ty UK Ltd.
Waterlooville, Hants
P08 8HH
© Ty Deutschland
90008 Nürnberg
Handmade in China

[Beanie Name]™ [Style Number]
to _____
from _____
with
love

....$150

4th Generation

The Beanie Babies™ Collection
© Ty Inc.
Oakbrook Il, U.S.A.
© Ty UK Ltd.
Fareham, Hants
P015 5TX
© Ty Deutschland
90008 Nürnberg
Handmade in China

[Beanie Name]™ [Style Number]
DATE OF BIRTH: [Month-Day-Year]

[Beanie Poem]

Visit our web page!!!
http://www.ty.com

....$125

Item #:	4091
Issued:	1995
Retired:	5/97
Birthday:	10/30/95
Poem:	Radar the bat flies late at night
	He can soar to an amazing height
	If you see something as high as a star
	Take a good look, it might be Radar!

Rex the Tyrannosaurus

3rd Generation

The Beanie Babies™ Collection

Ⓒ Ty Inc.
Oakbrook IL. U.S.A.

Ⓒ Ty UK Ltd.
Waterlooville, Hants
PO8 8HH

Ⓒ Ty Deutschland
90008 Nürnberg
Handmade in China

[Beanie Name]™ [Style Number]

to _____

from _____

with

love

.... $700

Item #:	4086
Issued:	1995
Retired:	1996
Birthday:	Unknown
Poem:	None

Righty the Elephant

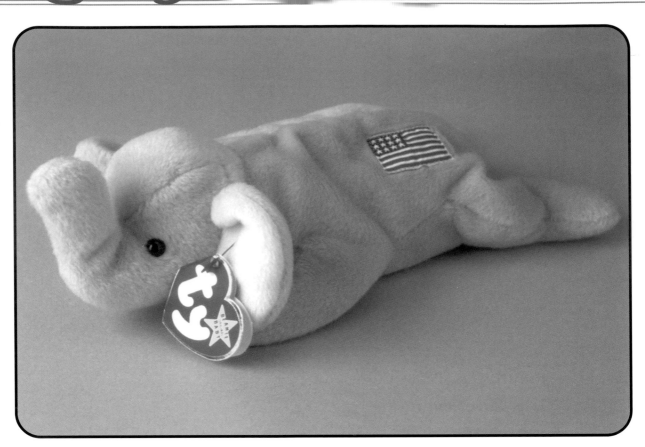

4th Generation

with flag $280
without flag $280

Item #:	4086
Issued:	1996
Retired:	1/97
Birthday:	7/4/96
Poem:	Donkeys to the left, elephants to the right
	Often seems like a crazy sight
	This whole game seems very funny
	Until you realize they're spending your money!

Ringo *the* Raccoon

3rd Generation

The Beanie Babies™ Collection
Ⓒ Ty Inc.
Oakbrook IL. U.S.A.
Ⓒ Ty UK Ltd.
Waterlooville, Hants
PO8 8HH
Ⓒ Ty Deutschland
90008 Nürnberg
Handmade in China

[Beanie Name]™ [Style Number]
to _____
from _____
with
love

. . . . $33.00

4th Generation

The Beanie Babies™ Collection
Ⓒ Ty Inc.
Oakbrook IL. U.S.A.
Ⓒ Ty UK Ltd.
Fareham, Hants
PO15 5TX
Ⓒ Ty Deutschland
90008 Nürnberg
Handmade in China

[Beanie Name]™ [Style Number]
DATE OF BIRTH : [Month-Day-Year]

[Beanie Poem]

Visit our web page!!!
http://www.ty.com

. . . . $5.50

Item #:	4014
Issued:	1995
Birthday:	7/14/95
Poem:	Ringo hides behind his mask He will come out, if you should ask He loves to chitter, he loves to chatter Just about anything, it doesn't matter!

Roary the Lion

4th Generation

$5.50

Item #:	4069
Issued:	1997
Birthday:	2/20/96
Poem:	Deep in the jungle they crowned him king
	But being brave is not his thing
	A cowardly lion some may say
	He hears his roar and runs away!

Rover the Red Dog

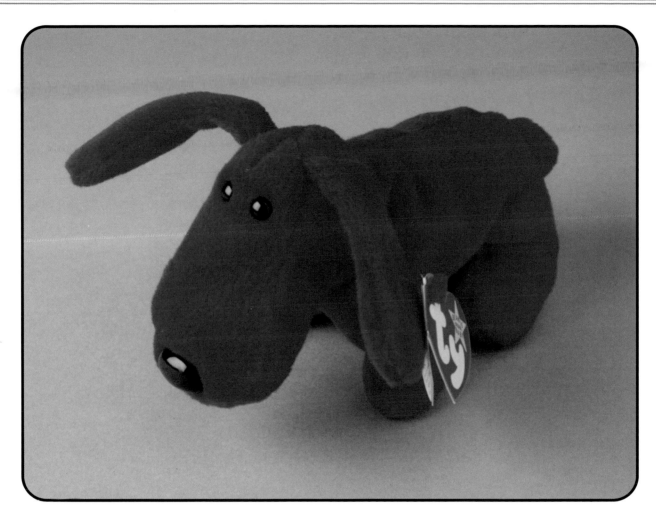

4th Generation

The Beanie Babies™ Collection

® Ty Inc.
Oakbrook IL, U.S.A.

® Ty UK Ltd.
Fareham, Hants
PO15 5TX

® Ty Deutschland
90908 Nürnberg

Handmade in China

[Beanie Name]™ [Style Number]
DATE OF BIRTH : [Month-Day-Year]

[Beanie Poem]

Visit our web page!!!
http://www.ty.com

.... $5.50

Item #:	4101
Issued:	1996
Birthday:	5/30/96
Poem:	This dog is red and his name is Rover
	If you call him he is sure to come over
	He barks and plays with all his might
	But worry not, he won't bite!

Scoop *the* Pelican

4th Generation

ty

The Beanie Babies™ Collection
① Ty Inc.
   Oakbrook IL, U.S.A.
① Ty UK Ltd.
   Fareham, Hants
   PO15 5TX
① Ty Deutschland
   90008 Nürnberg
   Handmade in China

[Beanie Name]™ [Style Number]
DATE OF BIRTH [Month-Day-Year]

[Beanie Poem]

Visit our web page!!!
http://www.ty.com

.... $6.00

Item #:	4107
Issued:	1996
Birthday:	7/1/96
Poem:	All day long he scoops up fish
	To fill his bill, is his wish
	Diving fast and diving low
	Hoping those fish are very slow

Scottie the Black Terrier

4th Generation

The Beanie Babies™ Collection

® Ty Inc.
Oakbrook IL. U.S.A.
® Ty UK Ltd.
Fareham, Hants
PO15 5TX
® Ty Deutschland
90008 Nürnberg
Handmade in China

[Beanie Name]™ [Style Number]
DATE OF BIRTH: [Month-Day-Year]

[Beanie Poem]

Visit our web page!!!
http://www.ty.com

.... $5.50

Item #:	4102
Issued:	1996
Birthday:	6/15/96
Poem:	Scottie is a friendly sort
	Even though his legs are short
	He is always happy as can be
	His best friends are you and me!

Seamore *the White Seal*

1st Generation $190

2nd Generation $170

3rd Generation $150

4th Generation $150

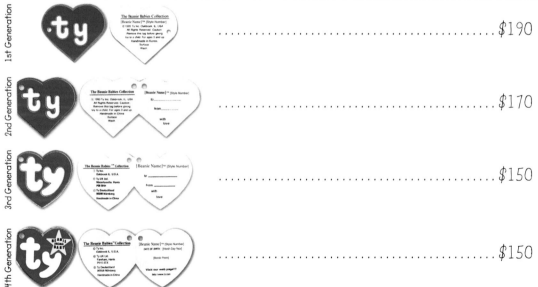

Item #:	4029
Issued:	1995
Retired:	10/97
Birthday:	12/14/96
Poem:	Seamore is a little white seal
	Fish and clams are her favorite meal
	Playing and laughing in the sand
	She's the happiest seal in the land!

Seaweed *the Otter*

3rd Generation

The Beanie Babies™ Collection   [Beanie Name]™ [Style Number]

ⓒ Ty Inc.
Oakbrook IL. U.S.A.
ⓒ Ty UK Ltd.
Waterlooville, Hants
P08 8HH
ⓒ Ty Deutschland
90008 Nürnberg
Handmade in China

to _____
from _____
with
love

.... $28.00

4th Generation

The Beanie Babies™ Collection   [Beanie Name]™ [Style Number]
DATE OF BIRTH: [Month-Day-Year]

ⓒ Ty Inc.
Oakbrook IL. U.S.A.
ⓒ Ty UK Ltd.
Fareham, Hants
P015 5TX
ⓒ Ty Deutschland
90008 Nürnberg
Handmade in China

[Beanie Poem]

Visit our web page!!!
http://www.ty.com

.... $5.50

Item #:	4080
Issued:	1996
Birthday:	3/19/96
Poem:	Seaweed is what she likes to eat It's supposed to be a delicious treat Have you tried a treat from the water? If you haven't, maybe you "otter"!

Slither the Snake

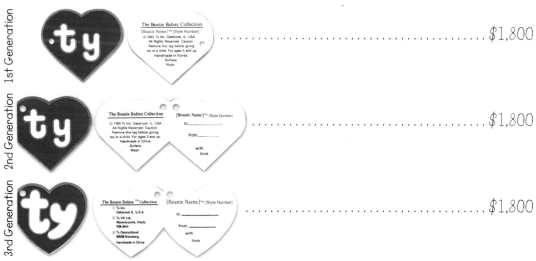

1st Generation

The Beanie Babies Collection
[Beanie Name]™ [Style Number]
© 1993 Ty Inc. Oakbrook, IL USA
All Rights Reserved. Caution
Remove this tag before giving
toy to a child. For ages 5 and up.
Handmade in Korea
Surface
Wash

.... $1,800

2nd Generation

The Beanie Babies Collection
© 1993 Ty Inc. Oakbrook, IL. USA
All Rights Reserved. Caution
Remove this tag before giving
toy to a child. For ages 3 and up.
Handmade in China
Surface
Wash.

[Beanie Name]™ [Style Number]
to _____
from _____
with
love

.... $1,800

3rd Generation

The Beanie Babies ™ Collection
© Ty Inc.
Oakbrook, IL U.S.A.
© Ty UK Ltd.
Waterlooville, Hants
PO8 8HH
© Ty Deutschland
90008 Nürnberg
Handmade in China

[Beanie Name]™ [Style Number]
to _____
from _____
with
love

.... $1,800

Item #:	4031
Issued:	1994
Retired:	1996
Birthday:	Unknown
Poem:	None

Sly the Fox

The Beanie Babies™ Collection
© Ty Inc.
Oakbrook IL. U.S.A.
℗ Ty UK Ltd.
Fareham, Hants
PO15 5TX
℗ Ty Deutschland
90008 Nürnberg
Handmade in China

[Beanie Name]™ [Style Number]
DATE OF BIRTH : [Month-Day-Year]

[Beanie Poem]

Visit our web page!!!
http://www.ty.com

Brown belly $80.00
White belly $5.50

Item #:	4115
Issued:	1996
Birthday:	9/12/96
Poem:	Sly is a fox and tricky is he Please don't chase him, let him be If you want him, just say when He'll peek out from his den!

Snip *the* Siamese Cat

4th Generation

The Beanie Babies™ Collection

① Ty Inc.
Oakbrook IL. U.S.A.

② Ty UK Ltd.
Fareham, Hants
PO15 5TX

③ Ty Deutschland
90008 Nürnberg

Handmade in China

[Beanie Name]™ [Style Number]

DATE OF BIRTH: [Month-Day-Year]

[Beanie Poem]

Visit our web page!!!
http://www.ty.com

.... $6.00

Item #:	4120
Issued:	1997
Birthday:	10/22/96
Poem:	Snip the cat is Siamese
	She'll be your friend if you please
	So toss her a toy or a piece of string
	Playing with you is her favorite thing.

Snort the Bull

4th Generation

The Beanie Babies™ Collection

© Ty Inc.
Oakbrook IL, U.S.A.

© Ty UK Ltd.
Fareham, Hants
PO15 5TX

© Ty Deutschland
90008 Nürnberg
Handmade in China

[Beanie Name]™ [Style Number]
DATE OF BIRTH: [Month-Day-Year]

[Beanie Poem]

Visit our web page!!!
http://www.ty.com

. . . . $7.00

Item #:	4002
Issued:	1996
Birthday:	5/15/95
Poem:	Although Snort is not so tall He loves to play basketball He is a star player in his dreams Can you guess his favorite team?

Snowball *the Snowman*

4th Generation

ty
BEANIE
ORIGINAL
BABY

The Beanie Babies™ Collection

® Ty Inc.
Oakbrook IL, U.S.A.

® Ty UK Ltd.
Fareham, Hants
PO15 5TX

® Ty Deutschland
90008 Nürnberg

Handmade in China

[Beanie Name]™ [Style Number]
DATE OF BIRTH: [Month-Day-Year]

[Beanie Poem]

Visit our web page!!!
http://www.ty.com

. . . . $25.00

Item #:	4201
Issued:	1997
Retired:	1/98
Birthday:	12/22/96
Poem:	There is a snowman, I've been told
	That plays with Beanies out in the cold
	What is better in a winter wonderland
	Than a Beanie snowman in your hand!

Sparky *the Dalmation*

4th Generation

The Beanie Babies™ Collection

ⓡ Ty Inc.
Oakbrook IL. U.S.A.

ⓡ Ty UK Ltd.
Fareham, Hants
PO15 5TX

ⓡ Ty Deutschland
90008 Nürnberg

Handmade in China

[Beanie Name]™ [Style Number]

DATE OF BIRTH : [Month-Day-Year]

[Beanie Poem]

Visit our web page!!!
http://www.ty.com

. . . . $110

Item #:	4100
Issued:	1996
Retired:	5/97
Birthday:	2/27/96
Poem:	Sparky rides proud on the firetruck
	Ringing the bell and pushing his luck
	He gets underfoot when trying to help
	He often gets stepped on and
	Lets out a yelp!

Speedy *the* Turtle

Item #:	4030
Issued:	1994
Retired:	10/97
Birthday:	8/14/94
Poem:	Speedy ran marathons in the past
	Such a shame, always last
	Now Speedy is a big star
	After he bought a racing car.

Spike *the* Rhinoceros

4th Generation

The Beanie Babies™ Collection

® Ty Inc.
Oakbrook IL. U.S.A.

® Ty UK Ltd.
Fareham, Hants
PO15 5TX

® Ty Deutschland
90008 Nürnberg

Handmade in China

[Beanie Name]™ [Style Number]

DATE OF BIRTH: [Month-Day-Year]

[Beanie Poem]

Visit our web page!!!
http://www.ty.com

. . . . $6.00

Item #:	4060
Issued:	1996
Birthday:	8/13/96
Poem:	Spike the rhino likes to stampede He's the bruiser that you need Gentle to birds on his back and spike You can be his friend if you like!

Spinner *the* Spider

.... $10.00

Item #:	4036
Issued:	1997
Birthday:	10/28/96
Poem:	Does this spider make you scared? Among many people that feeling is shared Remember spiders have feelings too In fact, this spider really likes you!

Splash the Orca Whale

Item #:   4022
Issued: 1994
Retired: 5/97
Birthday: 7/8/93
Poem: Splash loves to jump and dive
            He's the fastest whale alive
            He always wins the 100 yard dash
            With a victory jump he'll make a splash!

Spooky *the Ghost*

Item #:	4090
Issued:	1995
Retired:	1/98
Birthday:	10/31/95
Poem:	Ghosts can be a scary sight
	But don't let Spooky bring you any fright
	Because when you're alone, you will see
	The best friend that Spooky can be!

Spot the Black and White Dog

Old - Without Spot

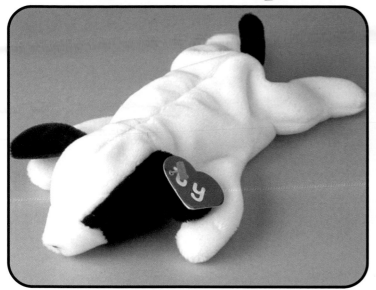

New - With Spot

1st Generation	.ty	without spot $985
2nd Generation	ty	without spot .... $985 with spot................................... $40
3rd Generation	ty	with spot................................... $40
4th Generation	ty	with spot................................... $35

Item #:	4000
Issued:	1994
Retired:	10/97
Birthday:	1/3/93
Poem:	See Spot sprint, see Spot run You and Spot will have lots of fun Watch out now, because he's not slow Just stand back and watch him go!

Squealer the Pig

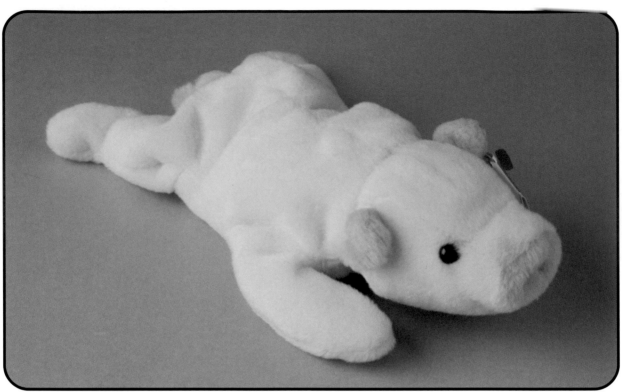

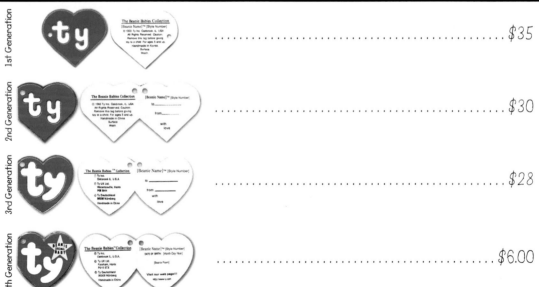

Item #:	4005
Issued:	1994
Birthday:	4/23/93

Poem: Squealer likes to joke around
He is known as class clown
Listen to his stories awhile
There is not doubt he will make you smile!

Steg *the Stegosaurus*

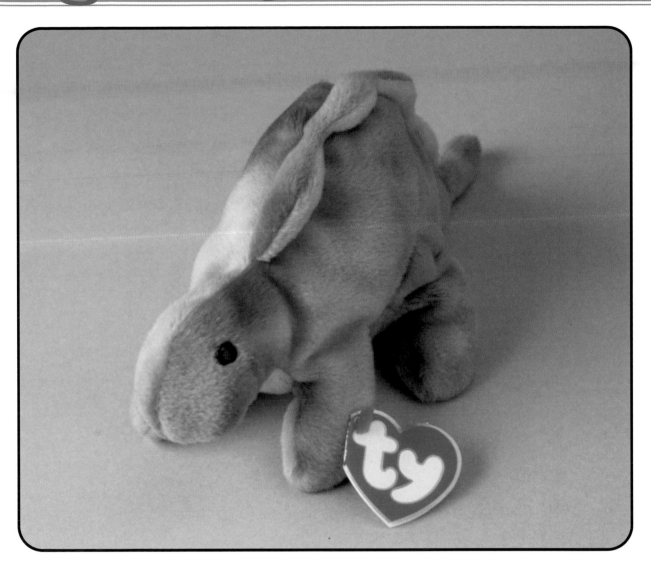

3rd Generation

The Beanie Babies ™ Collection

① Ty Inc.
Oakbrook IL, U.S.A.
② Ty UK Ltd.
Waterlooville, Hants
PO8 8HH
③ Ty Deutschland
90008 Nürnberg
Handmade in China

[Beanie Name]™ [Style Number]

to _____
from _____
with
love

.... $900

Item #:	4087
Issued:	1995
Retired:	1996
Birthday:	Unknown
Poem:	None

Sting *the Manta Ray*

3rd Generation $190

4th Generation $180

Item #:	4077
Issued:	1995
Retired:	1/97
Birthday:	8/27/95
Poem:	I'm a manta ray and my name is Sting
	I'm quite unusual and this is the thing
	Under the water I glide like a bird
	Have you ever seen something so absurd?

Stinky *the Skunk*

Item #:	4017
Issued:	1995
Birthday:	2/13/95
Poem:	Deep in the woods he lived in a cave
	Perfume and mints were the gifts he gave
	He showered every night in the kitchen sink
	Hoping one day he wouldn't stink!

Stripes *the Tiger*

Old - Dark w/more stripes   New - Light w/less stripes

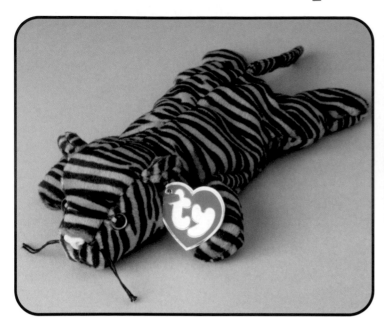

3rd Generation

Old version $160
Fuzzy belly $80

4th Generation

New version $5.50

Item #:	4065
Issued:	1995
Birthday:	6/11/95
Poem:	Stripes was never fierce nor strong
	So with tigers, he didn't get along
	Jungle life was hard to get by
	So he came to his friends at Ty.

Strut the Rooster

4th Generation

.... $10

Item #:	4171
Issued:	1997
Birthday:	3/8/96
Poem:	Listen closely to "Cock-a-doodle-doo" What's the rooster saying to you? Hurry, wake up sleepy head We have lots to do, get out of bed!

Tabasco the Bull

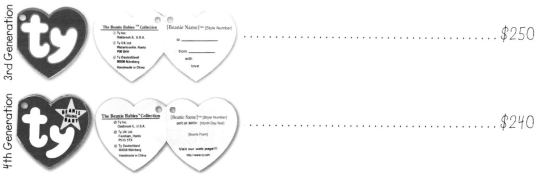

3rd Generation

The Beanie Babies™ Collection

① Ty Inc.
Oakbrook IL, U.S.A.
② Ty UK Ltd.
Waterlooville, Hants
PO8 8HN
③ Ty Deutschland
90008 Nürnberg
Handmade in China

[Beanie Name]™ [Style Number]

to _____
from _____
with
love

.... $250

4th Generation

The Beanie Babies™ Collection

① Ty Inc.
Oakbrook IL, U.S.A.
② Ty UK Ltd.
Fareham, Hants
PO15 5TX
③ Ty Deutschland
90008 Nürnberg
Handmade in China

[Beanie Name]™ [Style Number]
DATE OF BIRTH: [Month-Day-Year]

[Beanie Poem]

Visit our web page!!!
http://www.ty.com

.... $240

Item #:	4002
Issued:	1995
Retired:	1/97
Birthday:	5/15/95
Poem:	Although Tabasco is not so tall
	He loves to play basketball
	He is a star player in his dream
	Can you guess his favorite team?

Tank the Armadillo

Old - No Shell
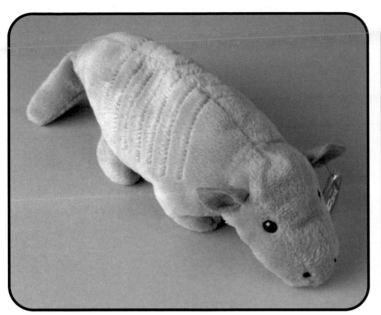

New - With Shell

3rd Generation

7 rows.................................$90

4th Generation

9 rows, no shell......................$90
with shell.............................$75

Item #:   4031
Issued: 1995
Retired: 10/97
Birthday: 2/22/95
Poem: This armadillo lives in the South
             Shoving Tex-Mex in his mouth
             He sure loves it south of the border
             Keeping his friends in good order!

1997 Teddy

$30

Item #:	4200
Issued:	1997
Retired:	1/98
Birthday:	12/25/96
Poem:	Beanie Babies are special no doubt
	All filled with love - inside and out
	Wishes for fun times filled with joy
	Ty's holiday teddy is a magical toy!

Teddy *the Brown Teddy Bear*

Old - Old Face

New - New Face

1st Generation		Old face $2,500
2nd Generation		Old face .... $2,500 New face $125
3rd Generation		New face $120
4th Generation		New face $75

Item #:	4050
Issued:	1994
Retired:	10/97
Birthday:	11/28/95
Poem:	Teddy wanted to go out today But all his friends went out to play But he'd rather help whatever you do After all, his best friend is you!

Teddy *the Cranberry Teddy Bear*

Old Face (left) New Face (right)

1st Generation		Old face	$1,700
2nd Generation		Old face	$1,600
		New face	$1,500
3rd Generation		New Face	$1,500

Item #:	4052
Issued:	1994
Retired:	1996
Birthday:	Unknown
Poem:	None

Teddy the Jade Teddy Bear

Old Face (left) New Face (right)

1st Generation	Old face	..................................$1,600
2nd Generation	Old face	..................................$1,600
	New face	..................................$1,500
3rd Generation	New Face	..................................$1,500

Item #:   4057

Issued: 1994

Retired: 1996

Birthday: Unknown

Poem: None

Teddy *the Magenta Teddy Bear*

Old Face (left) New Face (right)

Old face $1,600

Old face $1,600

New face $1,500

New Face $1,500

Item #:	4056
Issued:	1994
Retired:	1996
Birthday:	Unknown
Poem:	None

Teddy *the Teal Teddy Bear*

Old Face (left) New Face (right)

Old face $1,600

Old face $1,600
New face $1,500

New Face $1,500

Item #:	4051
Issued:	1994
Retired:	1996
Birthday:	Unknown
Poem:	None

Old Face (left) New Face (right)

1st Generation

Old face $1,600

2nd Generation

Old face $1,600

New face $1,500

3rd Generation

New Face $1,500

Item #:	4055
Issued:	1994
Retired:	1996
Birthday:	Unknown
Poem:	None

Trap the Mouse

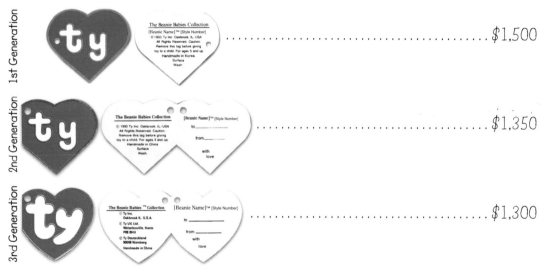
Trap the Mouse

Item #:	4042
Issued:	1994
Retired:	1996
Birthday:	Unknown
Poem:	None

Tuffy the Brown Terrier

.... $5.50

Item #:	4108
Issued:	1997
Birthday:	10/12/96
Poem:	Taking off with a thunderous blast
	Tuffy rides his motorcycle fast
	The Beanies roll with laughs and squeals
	He never took off his training wheels!

Tusk the Walrus

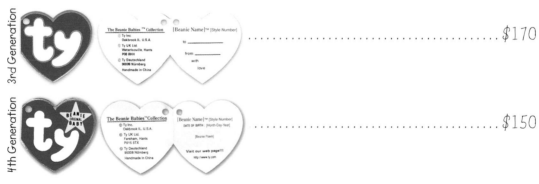

Item #:	4076
Issued:	1995
Birthday:	Unknown
Retired:	1/97
Poem:	Tusk brushes his teeth everyday To keep them shiny, it's the only way Teeth are special, so you must try And they will sparkle when you say "Hi"!

Twigs the Giraffe

Item #:   4068

Issued: 1995

Birthday: 5/19/95

Poem: Twigs has his head in the clouds
             He stands tall, he stands proud
             With legs so skinny they wobble and shake
             What an unusual friend he will make!

Valentino the Bear

 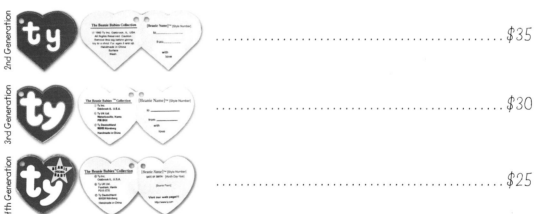
Item #:	4058
Issued:	1994
Birthday:	2/14/94
Poem:	His heart is red and full of love
	He cares for you so give him a hug
	Keep him close when feeling blue
	Feel the love he has for you!

Velvet the Panther

 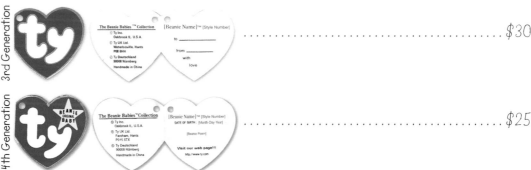
Item #:	4064
Issued:	1995
Retired:	10/97
Birthday:	12/16/95
Poem:	Velvet loves to sleep in the trees
	Lulled to dreams by the buzz of the bees
	She snoozes all day and plays all night
	Running and jumping in the moonlight!

Waddle the Penguin

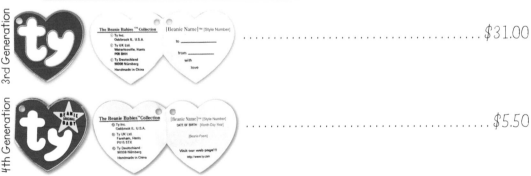

3rd Generation — The Beanie Babies™ Collection — [Beanie Name]™ [Style Number] $31.00

4th Generation — The Beanie Babies™ Collection — [Beanie Name]™ [Style Number] $5.50

Item #:	4075
Issued:	1995
Birthday:	12/19/95
Poem:	Waddle the penguin likes to dress up Every night he wears his tux When Waddle walks, it never fails He always trips over his tails!

Waves *the Orca Whale*

4th Generation

The Beanie Babies™ Collection

® Ty Inc.
Oakbrook IL, U.S.A.

® Ty UK Ltd.
Fareham, Hants
PO15 5TX

® Ty Deutschland
90008 Nürnberg
Handmade in China

[Beanie Name]™ [Style Number]
DATE OF BIRTH : [Month-Day-Year]

[Beanie Poem]

Visit our web page!!!
http://www.ty.com

.... $5.50

Item #:	4084
Issued:	1997
Birthday:	12/8/96
Poem:	Join him today on the Internet
	Don't be afraid to get your feet wet
	He taught all the Beanies how to surf
	Our web page is his home turf!

Web the Spider

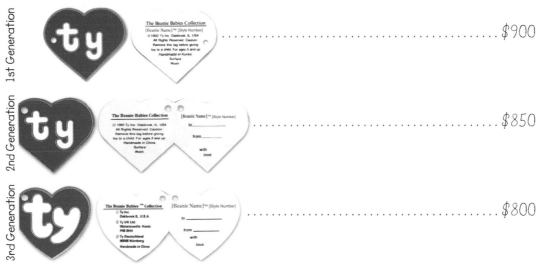

1st Generation $900

2nd Generation $850

3rd Generation $800

Item #:	4041
Issued:	1994
Retired:	1996
Birthday:	Unknown
Poem:	None

Weenie the Dachshund

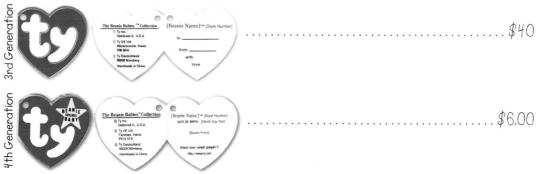

3rd Generation $40

4th Generation $6.00

Item #:   4013

Issued: 1996

Birthday: 7/20/95

Poem: Weenie the dog is quite a sight
             Long of body and short of height
             He perches himself high on a log
             And considers himself to be top dog!

Wrinkles *the Bulldog*

The Beanie Babies™ Collection

© Ty Inc.
Oakbrook IL, U.S.A.

© Ty UK Ltd.
Fareham, Hants
PO15 5TX

© Ty Deutschland
90008 Nürnberg

Handmade in China

[Beanie Name]™ [Style Number]

DATE OF BIRTH   [Month-Day-Year]

[Beanie Poem]

Visit our web page!!!
http://www.ty.com

.... $5.50

Item #:	4103
Issued:	1996
Birthday:	5/1/96
Poem:	This little dog is named Wrinkles
	His nose is soft and often crinkles
	Likes to climb up on your lap
	He's a cheery sort of chap!

Ziggy the Zebra

3rd Generation

The Beanie Babies™ Collection
Ⓒ Ty Inc.
Oakbrook IL, U.S.A.
Ⓒ Ty UK Ltd.
Waterlooville, Hants
PO8 8HH
Ⓒ Ty Deutschland
90008 Nürnberg
Handmade in China

[Beanie Name]™ [Style Number]
to _____
from _____
with
love
....$26

4th Generation

The Beanie Babies™ Collection
Ⓒ Ty Inc.
Oakbrook IL, U.S.A.
Ⓒ Ty UK Ltd.
Fareham, Hants
PO15 5TX
Ⓒ Ty Deutschland
90008 Nürnberg
Handmade in China

[Beanie Name]™ [Style Number]
DATE OF BIRTH : [Month-Day-Year]

[Beanie Poem]

Visit our web page!!!
http://www.ty.com
....$5.50

Item #:	4063
Issued:	1995
Birthday:	12/24/95
Poem:	Ziggy likes soccer - he's a referee
	That way he watches the games for free
	The other Beanies don't think it's fair
	But Ziggy the zebra doesn't care.

Zip the Black Cat

Old - Black w/White Face & Belly

Old - All Black

New - Black w/White Paws

2nd Generation	white belly................................$190	
3rd Generation	white belly................................$190 all black................................$975 white paws................................$12.00	
4th Generation	white paws................................$6.00	

Item #:   4004

Issued: 1994

Birthday: 3/28/94

Poem: Keep Zip by your side all the day through
            Zip is good luck, you'll see it's true
            When you have something you need to do
            Zip will always believe in you!

Beanie Baby Collection of:

Your Name

Beanie	Price Paid	Value	Beanie	Price Paid	Value	Beanie	Price Paid	Value
❏ Ally			❏ Hippity			❏ Scotty		
❏ Baldy			❏ Hissy			❏ Seamore		
❏ Batty			❏ Hoot			❏ Seaweed		
❏ Bernie			❏ Hoppity			❏ Slither		
❏ Bessie			❏ Humphrey			❏ Sly		
❏ Blackie			❏ Iggy			❏ Smoochy		
❏ Blizzard			❏ Inch			❏ Snip		
❏ Bones			❏ Inky			❏ Snort		
❏ Bongo			❏ Jolly			❏ Snowball		
❏ Britannia			❏ Kiwi			❏ Sparky		
❏ Bronty			❏ Lefty			❏ Speedy		
❏ Brownie			❏ Legs			❏ Spike		
❏ Bruno			❏ Libearty			❏ Spinner		
❏ Bubbles			❏ Lizzy			❏ Splash		
❏ Bucky			❏ Lucky			❏ Spooky		
❏ Bumble			❏ Magic			❏ Spot		
❏ Caw			❏ Manny			❏ Spunky		
❏ Chilly			❏ Maple			❏ Squealer		
❏ Chip			❏ Mel			❏ Steg		
❏ Chocolate			❏ Mystic			❏ Sting		
❏ Chops			❏ Nana			❏ Stinky		
❏ Claude			(Original Bongo)			❏ Stretch		
❏ Congo			❏ Nanook			❏ Stripes		
❏ Coral			❏ Nip			❏ Strut		
❏ Crunch			❏ Nuts			❏ Tabasco		
❏ Cubbie			❏ Patti			❏ Tank		
❏ Curly			❏ Peace			❏ Teddy Brown		
❏ Daisy			❏ Peanut			❏ Teddy Cranberry		
❏ Derby			❏ Peking			❏ Teddy Jade		
❏ Digger			❏ Pinchers			❏ Teddy Magenta		
❏ Doby			❏ Pinky			❏ Teddy Teal		
❏ Doodle			❏ Pouch			❏ Teddy Violet		
❏ Dotty			❏ Pounce			❏ Teddy 1997		
❏ Ears			❏ Prance			❏ Trap		
❏ Echo			❏ Pride			❏ Tuffy		
❏ Flash			❏ Princess Bear			❏ Tusk		
❏ Fleece			❏ Puffer			❏ Twigs		
❏ Flip			❏ Pugsly			❏ Valentino		
❏ Floppity			❏ Quackers			❏ Velvet		
❏ Flutter			❏ Radar			❏ Waddle		
❏ Freckles			❏ Rainbow			❏ Waves		
❏ Garcia			❏ Rex			❏ Web		
❏ Gobbles			❏ Righty			❏ Weenie		
❏ Goldie			❏ Ringo			❏ Wrinkles		
❏ Gracie			❏ Roary			❏ Ziggy		
❏ Grunt			❏ Rover			❏ Zip		
❏ Happy			❏ Scoop					

Wish List

_____   _____   _____

_____   _____   _____

_____   _____   _____